Spot the Intro

1980s

Not just a great book...
...but also an addictive
musical quiz game too!

Welcome to the 1980s!

Inside this book you'll find an audio CD crammed with some 250 snippets of music for you to try and recognise. But what's more: the CD also contains hundreds of trivia questions on all aspects of the techno Eighties, from people to places, television to film.

Jam-packed into the book are fun and fascinating facts about the decade that saw the collapse of the Iron Curtain, the Falklands War, Royal Weddings and Thatcherism. Do you remember the race riots, the Stock Market Crash, Yuppies and Sloane Rangers? Were you at Live Aid; did you dress like Boy George; work out with Jane Fonda's video or guess 'Who Shot JR'? If so, you'll enjoy Spot The Intro 80s! Keep a look out for the 60s and 70s editions, the full CD Quiz Games, Spot The Intro Board Game and Spot The Intro DVD Game! Like this book, they are packed with a mixture of nostalgic trivia, music and fun!

Playing the CD game...

Divide into 2, 3 or 4 teams. Simply provide each team with a pen or pencil and a blank sheet of paper, then pop the CD into your compact disc player... and you're off!

The game is played over 9 rounds, each round being either a set of musical snippets for you to recognise or a set of trivia questions.

When everyone's ready, press 'Play' and listen to the five clips of music. At every 'Ping!' press 'Pause', allow everyone time in which to write down their answers, then swap answer sheets for marking - there's a score grid on page 57 and the answers from page 58. Ready again? Release the pause button and continue playing the CD - you'll now hear five trivia questions on 'Music' from this decade. Continue playing in this fashion through all 9 rounds. You should use tracks 1-9 the first time you play, then tracks 10-18 and so on.

Scoring your answers...

You'll find the answers to all tracks at the back of this book. In the Spot The Intro music clip rounds, score 1 point for each correctly identified song and 1 point for the correct artist or band. In the trivia rounds, score 2 points for each correct answer. You should use your discretion to award half marks where a given answer is judged to be partly correct - always err on the side of generosity!

Winning the game...

Add up the final scores; the team with the highest total is the winner! You can enter scores on the Team Score Grid on page 57 or - should you prefer - download score sheets from our website:

click: **www.cheatwell.com > downloads > STI score sheets**

eighties music

This decade was a melting-pot of musical styles, from the synth-pop of the New Romantics, Hi-NRG, Techno, Indie, Rap and Rave to re-issues from the '50s and '60s. With the arrival of the satellite channel, MTV, the demand for pop music was at an all time high. The public's insatiable appetite for music during this decade saw a rise in the production of 12 inch discs, picture discs and extended mixes whilst music magazines like NME and Melody Maker were essential reading for the music fan.

The advent of the Compact Disc saw record sales soar as back catalogues were transferred onto CD and people re-bought albums on disc. Eventually, however, the record industry saw a backlash as it was perceived to be greedy and complacent. Major labels were pilloried for sitting on their laurels and not championing more acts; a wave of independent record labels started up, with the acts themselves in control. Independent production companies such as Rough Trade, Beggar's Banquet and Factory brought 'indie' groups like The Smiths, Echo And The Bunnymen, The Cure and New Order to the public's attention and proved that bands such as these had a profitable niche alongside more traditional 'pop'.

new romantics

Emerging in the early Eighties, they were a direct back-lash against the severe, austere nature of the Punks. Whilst Punk was a working-class reaction against the establishment the Romantics followed a more hedonistic style. The genre took root in London's night clubs, particularly The Blitz which employed Steve Strange, Boy George and Marilyn as attendants. Similar to Glam Rock, with its androgynous style, New Romantic fashion and music were, however, distinctly different. David Bowie and Roxy Music are generally accepted as the originators of this trend but the key protagonists were bands such as Duran Duran, Spandau Ballet, Visage, Adam And The Ants, Ultravox and Culture Club. Other bands that made a significant contribution to the genre were ABC, Human League, Eurythmics, OMD and Depeche Mode.

techno

retro style

Synthesizers were introduced by various groups which began creating a new sound for the decade. This 'electro' sound developed rapidly and, as the decade progressed, formed the basis of 'techno', 'synth-pop' and 'Rap'. Groups such as Kraftwerk - who pioneered 'techno' - Depeche Mode and later Erasure became synonymous with the synthesizer and drum machine sound that characterised the 'techno' style. Other exponents of this 'electro' genre were acts such as Blancmange; Yazoo; Ultravox; New Order; Thomas Dolby; Howard Jones; Harold Faltermeyer; Human League; Jan Hammer and Soft Cell.

For part of this decade we saw a Fifties revival in both music and fashion. The American singer Jackie Wilson had a posthumous No.1 hit in 1986 with a re-issue of his 1957 song 'Reet Petite' whilst TV advertisements for jeans and other products used Fifties imagery to sell a lifestyle.

In one notable ad, singer Nick Kamen stripped down to his boxer shorts in a launderette to the tune of 'I Heard It Through The Grapevine' by Marvin Gaye. The advert significantly revived the fortunes of the jeans market!

hip-hop, scratching & rap

Hip-hop, as a style of music, originated in the United States during the mid-1970s in New York around Harlem and The Bronx; the genre becoming part of mainstream pop culture during the 1980s. Hip-Hop has two main components: rapping and scratching, a form of on-the-hoof mixing. Exponents of this genre were, amongst others, Sugarhill Gang, LL Cool J, Public Enemy and Grandmaster Flash. As Rap became mainstream so it was mixed with other music styles. Groups such as Run DMC added a heavy metal element whilst performers like MC Hammer incorporated dance routines.

At the same time white artists were getting in on the act including Vanilla Ice and The Beastie Boys. By the end of the decade Rap had moved into 'Gangsta' Rap where the lyrics were more sexually and violently explicit and spoke of gangland feuds and police hatred amongst Rap artists. Despite this, and maybe because of the controversy surrounding it, record sales soared until even 'Gangsta' Rap became mainstream in the next decade. Hip-Hop was as much a cultural movement as a music genre and incorporated dance styles, such as breakdancing, and street artistry ~ a high quality form of graffiti.

hostages

The six-day seige at the Iranian Embassy in London ends dramatically when live TV shows SAS soldiers storming the building to free 19 hostages. By contrast the US attempt to free their staff from the Iranian Embassy in Tehran ends in failure with a fatal accident in the desert.

1980

top flix

The Oscars:

Best Picture:
Ordinary People

Best Actor: Robert De Niro (Raging Bull)

Best Actress:
Sissy Spacek
(Coal Miner's Daughter)

Best Of The Rest:

The Blues Brothers;
The Empire Strikes Back;
Nine To Five;
The Shining;
Friday The 13th;
American Gigolo.

top tv

1. To The Manor Born
2. Dallas
3. This Is Your Life
4. My Wife Next Door
5. Jim'll Fix It

top pop

1. Don't Stand So Close To Me (The Police)
2. Woman In Love (Barbra Streisand)
3. Feels Like I'm In Love (Kelly Marie)
4. Super Trouper (ABBA)
5. D.I.S.C.O. (Ottawan)
6. The Tide Is High (Blondie)
7. Geno (Dexy's Midnight Runners)
8. Coward Of The County (Kenny Rogers)
9. Together We Are Beautiful (Fern Kinney)
10. (Just Like) Starting Over (John Lennon)

reagan

The former governor of California, Ronald Reagan, defeats Jimmy Carter to become the President of America. Reagan was a B-movie actor and starred in such classics as 'Bedtime For Bonzo'. Although ridiculed, Reagan was to become a formidable president, backed up by his ally Margaret Thatcher.

1980

lennon!

Lennon Is Dead!

On 9th December John Lennon is approached by a fan requesting an autograph as he leaves the Dakota Building where he lives in New York. The fan is Mark Chapman. Hours later as Lennon returns with Yoko, Chapman shoots Lennon dead. The world is shocked and saddened by this senseless murder.

iraq:iran

Encouraged by the USA the new dictator of Iraq, Saddam Hussein, orders his tanks into Iran following a history of border disputes. The war was to continue for 8 years and caused one million casualties. The Iraqi forces made extensive use of chemical weapons during the war.

demos

Almost 60,000 anti-nuclear demonstrators join CND on a peace march through London. The largest peace protest since CND began 22 years ago.

moscow

The Moscow Olympics are boycotted by many countries in July of this year - including the US, West Germany and Kenya - in protest over the USSR's invasion of Afghanistan. Seb Coe won the 1500m gold but was beaten by Steve Ovett in the 800m just days later.

acid house

Acid House evolved out of House music, a style of electronic dance music that was originally developed by DJs in Chicago in the '70s and '80s. It was notable for its pounding rhythms and drum machines and became popular in the UK towards the end of the decade. Whilst House was being pioneered by clubs such as The Hacienda in Manchester it also found its mark in Ibiza, fast becoming a hedonistic party island. Acid House was at its height during the period 1988–91. Dubbed The Second Summer of Love, these years saw this almost addictive form of dance music driving youth culture forward at a pace with raves ~ huge unlicensed, underground dance parties ~ popping up everywhere. Raves were high energy events and the participants were frequently fuelled by a cocktail of drugs, the most popular being MDMA or Ecstasy. Indeed drug culture blossomed again with even discredited substances such as LSD making a come back. Acts that were associated with the Rave scene included The KLF, The Shamen and Dmob. A yellow smiley face was adopted as the friendly face of Acid which influenced the music scene well into the '90s!

bands & singers

Wham!

Two school friends, George Michael and Andrew Ridgeley, bounced into the charts in 1982 with 'Young Guns (Go For It)' which reached the heady heights of No. 3. 'Wake Me Up Before You Go Go' was one of four No. 1s they had during the Eighties, the other three being 'Freedom', 'I'm Your Man' and 'The Edge Of Heaven', all written and produced by George Michael. The pair split in 1986 after Michael had gone solo with 'Careless Whisper' and 'A Different Corner'.

Culture Club

Led by the flamboyant Boy George, this quartet's biggest hits were 'Do You Really Want To Hurt Me?' in 1982 and 'Karma Chameleon' in 1983. The latter was a million-seller in the UK and also a US No. 1. In 1984 they won both the Brit Award for 'Best Group' and a Grammy for 'Best New Artist'. Boy George's androgynous 'look' was copied by countless teenagers the world over - and it spawned a whole industry of dolls, make-up and clothes!

Duran Duran

One of the first of the New Romantic groups, Duran Duran was fronted by Simon Le Bon. The single, 'Girls On Film' put them firmly on the map - the video which accompanied this song was thought too sexually explicit for terrestrial TV and instead found a home on the newly launched MTV channel. Directed by Godley and Creme (of 10cc fame), the video brought Duran Duran superstar status on both sides of the Atlantic. In 1983 their single, 'Is There Something I Should Know' went straight in at No. 1 and in 1984 'The Reflex' also reached No. 1, both in the UK and the States. Duran Duran are still performing and recording after more than 25 years in the music industry!

Spandau Ballet

Another key New Romantic group, Spandau Ballet came to public attention in 1980 with 'To Cut A Long Story Short', which reached No. 5. From 1980 to 1989 they had twenty chart entries of which ten went Top-10; their only No. 1 hit, however, was 'True' in 1983.

Eurythmics

Rising from the ashes of 'The Tourists', this innovative duo of Scottish vocalist Annie Lennox and singer/songwriter/ instrumentalist Dave Stewart re-invented themselves as Eurythmics in 1981. They went on to become the most charted male/female duo in the UK. 'Sweet Dreams' gave them a UK No. 2 plus a US No. 1 in 1983 followed by five Top 10 hits including 'Sexcrime'. They had their only UK No. 1 of the decade in 1985 with 'There Must Be An Angel (Playing With My Heart)', which featured the legendary Stevie Wonder on harmonica.

Simple Minds

Formed from ex-members of punk band Johnny & The Self Abusers, Jim Kerr was the lead singer. Taking their name from a line in a David Bowie song (Jean Genie), they became the most successful Scottish band of the decade, having five albums enter the UK chart at No. 1 and worldwide sales of over 30 million. Simple Minds became known as a stadium band and their anthemic radio-friendly songs included 'Don't You (Forget About Me)', 'Alive And Kicking', 'Sanctify Yourself', 'All The Things She Said', and UK No.1 'Belfast Child'. In 1984, Jim Kerr met and married Chrissie Hynde, the lead singer of The Pretenders, forming the ultimate pop partnership. The union was shortlived.

U2

These giants of rock entered the UK charts in 1981 and went on to have ten Top 10 hits during the decade including one UK and two US No. 1s. When Bono (as vocalist) and The Edge (as lead guitar) performed at Live Aid in the summer of '85 they won a massive new audience of people around the world and gained a reputation for dramatic stadium shows. U2 are, without doubt, one of the world's few 'supergroups'.

Adam & The Ants

'Ant Music' was all the rage at the start of the decade. Fans sported war paint across the nose and pirate outfits similar to those worn by Adam (Stuart Goddard) and his fellow Ants. They were 1981's top chart act and gave us such classics as 'Kings Of The Wild Frontier', 'Stand And Deliver', 'Prince Charming' and 'Ant Rap'. Their videos were elaborate, looking more like period dramas than pop videos. With the emphasis on panto, their tongues were firmly embedded in cheeks!

Madonna

Born Madonna Louise Ciccone in 1958, Madonna went on to become the most successful female chart act of all time in both the UK and US. Her first UK chart entry was 'Holiday' in 1984, which was one of twenty-two songs she released during the Eighties; six of these went to No. 1 whilst a further fourteen reached the Top 5!

The Smiths

Signed to the Rough Trade record label, The Smiths were one of the most popular 'indie' groups of the Eighties. With morose-sounding lead singer Morrissey, The Smiths were popular with students and angst-ridden teenagers alike. Key songs were 'What Difference Does It Make?', 'Panic', 'Heaven Knows I'm Miserable Now' and 'Shoplifters Of The World Unite'.

Bros

Featuring blonde-haired twins Matt and Luke Goss, Bros had a very successful spell in the charts. Adored by teenage girls, the boys were poster pin-ups. Their first hit 'When Will I Be Famous?' reached No. 2 followed by four more Top 5 hits including their only No. 1, 'I Owe You Nothing'. They won the Brits 'Best Newcomer' Award in 1988. Third band member, Craig Logan, then left the group with (reportedly) a £1 million pay off whilst the twins carried on until 1991.

Prince

Born Prince Rogers Nelson in 1958 in Minneapolis this singer/songwriter first entered the UK charts in 1980 with 'I Wanna Be Your Lover' and went on to have consistent chart success throughout the decade, including eight Top Ten UK hits. Prince is highly innovative and profoundly eccentric ~ not only has he recorded under his own name but also as 'The Artist Formerly Known As Prince' and, equally bizarrely, as a symbol.

Bon Jovi

The epitome of Eighties stadium rock, this New Jersey group's biggest UK hit of this decade was 'Livin' On A Prayer' in 1986.

Frankie Goes To Hollywood

Controversy and hype surrounded this successful five-piece group from Merseyside fronted by Holly Johnson. They were the first act since Gerry & The Pacemakers in 1963 to reach No. 1 with their first three chart entries. On the radio, one song in particular became famous for being banned from airplay by Radio One...it was deemed 'obscene'! The song was 'Relax' which (in spite of - or possibly because of the ban!) went straight to No. 1.

Other top acts of note include:

The Thompson Twins, A-ha, Bananarama, The Bangles and Whitney Houston.

wedding!

Charles Weds Diana!

Dubbed 'The Wedding Of The Century', Prince Charles marries Lady Diana Spencer at St. Paul's Cathedral in London. The union is watched by an estimated 700 million people around the world and by some 39 million in the UK alone.

1981

pope shot!

Pope John Paul II is shot by a Turkish assassin Mehmet Ali Agca during his weekly audience in St. Peter's Square. After a five hour operation the pontiff pulls through. Agca is jailed until 2006.

reagan

Reagan Shot!

President Reagan survives an assassin's six bullets outside a Washington hotel. The attacker is John Hinkley III, a 25 year old disc jockey. One bullet hits Reagan's left lung, inches from his heart. In hospital, the charismatic Reagan asks his doctors if they are Republicans.

ripper

The infamous Yorkshire Ripper, Peter Sutcliffe - responsible for at least thirteen murders - is found guilty of murder and sentenced to life imprisonment.

oh la la!

Guillotine Given The Chop By France

Astonishingly it is only in this year that France actually abolishes the death penalty and with it Madame Guillotine!

new party!

A new political party is formed by four disillusioned Labour politicians. Former Cabinet Ministers Shirley Williams, Roy Jenkins, David Owen and Bill Rogers resigned from the Parliamentary Labour Party to form the SDP or Social Democratic Party.

1981

top flix

The Oscars:
Best Picture:
Chariots Of Fire
Best Actor: Henry Fonda (On Golden Pond)
Best Actress: Katherine Hepburn (On Golden Pond)
Best Of The Rest:
Superman II; Arthur; Raiders Of The Lost Ark, An American Werewolf In London.

top tv

1. The Benny Hill Show
2. This Is Your Life
3. Coronation Street
4. To The Manor Born
5. Shelley

top pop

1. Tainted Love (Soft Cell)
2. Stand And Deliver (Adam and the Ants)
3. Prince Charming (Adam and the Ants)
4. This Ole House (Shakin' Stevens)
5. Vienna (Ultravox)
6. Making Your Mind Up (Bucks Fizz)
7. One Day In Your Life (Michael Jackson)
8. Shaddup You Face (Joe Dolce Music Theatre)
9. Birdie Song (The Tweets)
10. You Drive Me Crazy (Shakin' Stevens)

Madness

Formed in '76, they originally performed under the band names The Invaders and Morris And The Minors. The band was part of the Ska revival of the late '70s but achieved near immortality during the '80s - in fact, Madness spent more weeks in the UK chart than any other group! Their distinctive sound produced a plethora of hits including 'Baggy Trousers', 'House Of Fun' and 'Our House'. Indeed, their hits are too numerous to list here! The band split in 1986 but reformed in the Nineties to perform a concert called 'Madstock' to over 75,000 fans!

Kate Bush

Another iconic female artist of the '80s, the elfin Bush had burst onto the scene in the late '70s with her ethereal song 'Wuthering Heights' and ground-breaking album 'The Kick Inside'. This unmistakable singer with an almost operatic range continued to release innovative music throughout the '80s and beyond.

King of Pop, **Michael Jackson,** was the youngest member of the teen band The Jackson Five. In 1979 Jackson embarked on what was to become a highly successful solo career. During the '80s Jackson recorded and co-produced the best-selling album of all time, 'Thriller' - It has sold over 100 million copies worldwide. Jackson was an influential figure and his musical innovation and eccentric nature coloured this decade.

Stock, Aitken & Waterman

Stock, Aitken & Waterman were a songwriting and record-producing trio who had great success during the mid-to-late '80s. Due to their production-line style and chart success the three are generally considered to be the most successful songwriting and production partnership of all time. They gained over 200 Top 40 UK hits in the mid-'80s to early '90s with acts like: Dead Or Alive, Bananarama, Rick Astley and soap stars Jason Donovan and Kylie Minogue.

Kylie Minogue

Rolling off the production line of the Stock- Aitken-Waterman hit factory, this former Aussie soap star launched her singing career with the catchy 'I Should Be So Lucky' in 1988 - her first No.1. From January 1988 to November 1989 Kylie had eight Top Five hits, including three No.1s.

UB40

Named after the unemployment benefit form, this Birmingham group had transatlantic success. With their Reggae sound, brothers Ali and Robin Campbell, together with Earl Falconer and assorted musicians had 27 chart entries during this decade, including two No. 1s. 'Red Red Wine' was both a UK and US No. 1 in 1983 and 'I Got You Babe', performed with Chrissie Hynde of The Pretenders, topped the charts in 1985. They collaborated with Hynde again in 1988 on 'Breakfast In Bed' which reached No. 6.

Bucks Fizz

Cheesy and manufactured, Bucks Fizz won the Eurovision Song Contest in 1981 with 'Making Your Mind Up'. When it reached No. 1 in the charts Bucks Fizz were dubbed Britain's answer to Abba! The group had two more No. 1s – 'The Land Of Make Believe' and 'My Camera Never Lies'. Following a fall-out, two separate Bucks Fizz bands went on to tour the club circuit for many years.

Howard Jones

This British singer/songwriter was a synthesizer king, often singing whilst surrounded by keyboards. His trademark coiffeur of spiked-up hair and catchy tunes made him popular both in the UK and US. His hits included 'New Song', 'What Is Love' and 'Like To Get To Know You Well'.

Dexy's Midnight Runners

This Birmingham post-punk group was led by Kevin Rowland. They burst into the charts in 1980 and soon had their first chart-topper with the single 'Geno'. In 1982 they had the year's top-selling UK single with 'Come On Eileen', which was a million-seller and also topped the US charts. An appearance on BBC's Top Of The Pops in 1982 is noteworthy due to the fact that when the group performed their song 'Jackie Wilson', the set designers mistakenly put up a large picture of darts player Jocky Wilson behind them on the stage!

gissa job!

The worst unemployment figures since the Great Depression of the 1930s, sees over 3 million people out of work. The Tory government holds power in a country where 1 in 8 people of working age are unemployed.

1982

gotcha!

Argentine forces invade the Falkland Islands in the South Atlantic. A task force is rapidly put together to retake the Islands and uphold British sovereignty. By 14th June the Islands are back in British hands and Argentina surrenders.

go 4 it!

On the 2nd November, Channel 4 is launched and begins broadcasting. The first show on air is the quiz show 'Countdown' hosted by Richard Whiteley.

we are...

The Queen wakes to find an intruder, Michael Fagan, in her bedroom at Buckingham Palace. Fagin stole a bottle of wine, lit a cigarette and chatted to the Queen, sitting on her bed until arrested!

wotta pair

Twickenham sees Erika Rowe streak across the pitch during the England v Australia rugby match, showing off her 40" assets to a hugely appreciative crowd!

up she rises

Henry VIII's flagship, the Mary Rose, is lifted out of its watery grave after 400 years lying on the sea bed. It is going to be preserved and then put on public display at Portsmouth's Historic Dockyard.

1982

top flix

The Oscars:
Best Picture: Gandhi
Best Actor: Ben Kingsley (Gandhi)
Best Actress: Meryl Streep (Sophie's Choice)
Best Of The Rest:
ET; Tootsie; Rocky III; An Officer And A Gentleman; Poltergeist; Tron, Blade Runner

other events

- Race riots flare up in Bristol's St. Paul's district
- Mark Thatcher gets lost in the Sahara during the Paris-Dakar rally.
- Princess Diana gives birth to her first son, Prince William.

top tv

1. Coronation Street
2. This Is Your Life
3. Hart To Hart
4. The Benny Hill Show
5. ITN News

top pop

1. Come On Eileen (Dexy's Midnight Runners)
2. Fame (Irene Cara)
3. Eye Of The Tiger (Survivor)
4. Do You Really Want To Hurt Me (Culture Club)
5. The Lion Sleeps Tonight (Tight Fit)
6. Pass The Dutchie (Musical Youth)
7. I Don't Wanna Dance (Eddy Grant)
8. Seven Tears (Goombay Dance Band)
9. Ebony & Ivory (Paul McCartney/Stevie Wonder)
10. Town Called Malice/Precious (The Jam)

fashion

The 1980s was a decade in which success and personal achievement were paramount. Even the clothes people wore were conspicuous, outward expressions of their success, be it in business with a 'designer' suit or attracting attention to a well-toned body (the result of hours dedicated to working out in a gym).

People were following the new 'get-rich-quick' credo in which application and hard work were believed to bring substantial rewards: the tag 'entrepreneur' became a buzz word.

Women were empowered as never before and their new-found confidence saw them 'dress for success' in the workplace. Women, no longer seen as the weaker sex, wore jackets with wide padded shoulders ~ a masculine shape but with additional feminine touches such as pastel colours and blouses with bows. The 'power suits' worn by Margaret Thatcher, the 'Iron Lady', epitomised this. She was a role model for many women, having achieved the highest position in politics, a career normally the preserve of men.

'Designer fashions' were very much a feature of this decade and those with 'loadsa money' sought out Calvin Klein, Ralph Lauren, Giorgio Armani, Donna Karan and Gianni Versace.

Men became interested in fashion too, and new high street retailers like Next brought affordable, fashionable clothes to 'yuppies'.

The American cop show 'Miami Vice' set a trend for men to wear their shiny suit jackets (with sleeves rolled up!) over a pastel T-shirt.

Teenagers and the 'yoof' market took their inspiration from pop music and style magazines such as The Face and I-D. The clothes worn by New Romantics, Madonna, Bananarama and Kylie, as well as the gender-bending Culture Club, led teenagers to experiment with their looks using lycra, leather, lace and frills topped off with bouffant hairstyles and make-up for both sexes! Slogan T-shirts were popularised after the fashion designer Katherine Hamnett turned up to meet

Margaret Thatcher wearing an anti-nuclear weapons T-shirt. It became fashionable to wear your protest on your chest and was adopted by many organisations.

American television soaps such as Dallas, Dynasty and The Colbys reinforced fashion trends such as shoulder pads and glamorous evening wear for women.

Throughout the decade there were also many unforgiveable fashion faux pas, not least of which were 'mullet' haircuts, 'shell suits', 'bolero jackets', 'leg warmers' and 'ra ra skirts'!!

fads & gadgets

The Mobile Phone

Could you survive without a mobile? It's surprising to think that the mobile phone barely existed before the '80s. This decade of one-upmanship witnessed wealthy Yuppies often become the first adopters of new technological advances, the mobile being one of them... but the first phones were bulky in comparison to today's offerings due to poor battery technology and network coverage.

Sony Walkman

The 'Walkman' was remarkable insomuch as, for the first time, a tape deck had been miniaturised, was easily portable and had reasonable sound quality. The radio and tape models were first on the scene followed by 'sport' and 'waterproof' editions which extended their appeal. It was one of the most successful consumer products of the decade. By 1984, the compact disc playing 'Discman' went on sale.

Pac Man

Pac Man originated in Japan where a computer firm called Namco Ltd based the game on a Japanese folk hero called Paku. Initially, the game was going to be called 'Puck-Man' until it was realised vandals could alter the letters to read something rude! Once the game had been licensed in America it became an even bigger success than its predecessor, Space Invaders. Later on, the computer games company Atari finally brought the game into people's homes.

Swatch Watches

These watches were introduced in '83. What was remarkable about them was that they were 80% cheaper to produce through fully automated assembly. With exciting designs that used plastics and bright graphics, they appealed to teenagers and Yuppies alike. The watches were highly affordable so people could buy different designs to match their outfits. They became such a fashionable item that new ranges saw devotees queuing up to buy the next generation.

Executive Desk Toys

Newton's Balls was the must-have desk toy of any executive worth his salt. A series of five chrome balls each suspended on nylon thread would provide a hypnotic, thought-provoking, mind-calming 'tick' when set in motion.

Pocket TVs

Casio launched the world's smallest television in 1983: the TV-10 had a 2.7" black & white liquid crystal display and was another must-have. In 1985 a colour version called TV-1000 was released.

Garfields

During the Eighties, the cartoon character Garfield, a cynical ginger cat, was widely syndicated. Garfield exhibited genuine human conditions such as apathy, boredom and worries about his weight and was soon hugely popular. Indeed, the comic strip is the most widely read strip of all time. Garfield merchandise popped up everywhere - particularly as a sucker-pawed cat stuck to car windows throughout Britain. Why? Nobody knows!

Aerobics & Workout Videos

Aerobics, which generally involves rapid stepping movements performed to music, took off in the '80s as people started to take an interest in their general fitness and well-being. Many celebrities - most notably Jane Fonda - produced videos or created TV shows which focused on this form of exercise. Aerobics spawned its own fashion trends including leg-warmers, headbands, off-the-shoulder sweaters and sports bras.

Dancing Flowers

Takara Rock 'n' Roll Dancing Flowers were all the rage! Battery-operated, the plastic table-top flowers would jiggle and bop in time to any music played next to them. Usually sporting sunglasses and holding musical instruments, this gadget amused and annoyed in equal measure.

Baby On Board

These high-visibility signs were mounted on the rear windscreen such that close-following motorists were aware that an infant was in the car. The signs originated, of course, in America as a genuine safety sign; however, they soon became a fad with joke versions being launched.

Filofax

A Filofax was an absolute-must for Yuppies: a compact leather bound, loose-leaf binder system, they kept contacts, calendars, diary entries and everything necessary for the go-getting entrepreneur. Around since 1921, their popularity took off when they were stocked by style-leader and British fashion designer Paul Smith in his shops.

Deely-Boppers

Deely-Boppers were a pair of glitzy, plastic balls stuck on the end of two long springs which were then attached to a head band. Nice!!!

space

The first US woman astronaut in space is Sally Ride, who returns to Earth aboard the space shuttle Challenger on June 24th having spent 8 days in orbit.

1983

cruisin'!

Hundreds of protesters, mainly women, start demonstrating outside the Greenham Common airbase and are arrested as the first US cruise missiles arrive. They subsequently form a semi-permanent campsite as a protest.

discs

The first CD players go on sale in the UK - but there are only 300 album titles available on CD!

£1 coin

The UK's one pound coin first comes into circulation on April 22nd.

bonza!

The Aussies win the America's Cup - it is the first time since 1870 that the American's have lost the sailing contest.

harrods bombed

The IRA explode a car bomb outside the Harrods department store in Knightsbridge during the Christmas shopping period. Six people lose their lives and a further ninety are seriously injured by the blast.

horse-napped

Champion racehorse, Shergar, winner of the 1981 Derby, is kidnapped and a £2 million ransom demanded.
The culprits are never caught and the horse is never seen again.

hitler diaries

The Sunday Times publishes the so-called Hitler Diaries, having paid a rumoured £1 million for the rights. Leading academics vouch for their authenticity until the diaries are exposed as a hoax and the Sunday Times is left with egg on its face!

1983

top flix

The Oscars:

Best Picture: Terms Of Endearment

Best Actor: Robert Duvall (Tender Mercies)

Best Actress: Shirley MacLaine (Terms Of Endearment)

Best Of The Rest:

The Return Of The Jedi; The Big Chill; Silkwood; Flashdance, Yentl

top tv

1. Coronation Street
2. This Is Your Life
3. It'll Be Alright On The Night
4. Last Of The Summer Wine
5. Family Fortunes

top pop

1. Karma Chameleon (Culture Club)
2. Uptown Girl (Billy Joel)
3. Red Red Wine (UB40)
4. Let's Dance (David Bowie)
5. Total Eclipse Of The Heart (Bonnie Tyler)
6. Down Under (Men At Work)
7. Billie Jean (Michael Jackson)
8. True (Spandau Ballet)
9. All Night Long (Lionel Richie)
10. You Can't Hurry Love (Phil Collins)

yuppies, dinkies & sloanes

In this decade the acronym came into its own ...and it's never looked back!

YUPPIES

The term Yuppie originated in America to describe 'Young Urban Professionals' or, moreso in the UK, 'Young Upwardly –mobile People'. The acronym inferred a selfish, avaricious and aggressively ambitious young executive and was used as both a term of praise and contempt. Yuppies were noted for their love of Filofaxes, mobile phones and red braces.

DINKY

Standing for 'Dual Income No Kids Yet', this term is used to describe a relatively high-earning couple who have chosen not to have (or possibly delayed having) children so that they may enjoy a more self-centred lifestyle.

NIMBY

From 'Not In My Back Yard', this acronym was coined to describe people who protested or opposed local developments which they felt inappropriate for their area. Often this protest arose through a fear of increased vulnerability or, more contentiously, a fear that house prices might drop! By definition, NIMBYs were quite happy for the development to occur elsewhere!

Sloane Rangers

Sloane Rangers (or 'Sloanes') were originally young upper-crust men & women living it up around London's Sloane Square. The term later became more associated with women, the most famous Sloane being Lady Diana Spencer. Men, with their loud boorish behaviour were dubbed Hooray Henries!

tv times

Breakfast TV

Before 1983 no TV was broadcast before midday! That all changed with the advent of Breakfast TV. The BBC launched 'Breakfast Time', hosted by Selina Scott & Frank Bough, two weeks ahead of the rival TV-AM (founded by Anna Ford, Michael Parkinson, Robert Key, Angela Rippon & David Frost). The similar formats of sweaters, sofas, keep-fit and cosy chat were slow to catch on. TV-AM hit financial troubles and the BBC shelved Breakfast Time, replacing it with BBC 'Breakfast News', before morning TV caught on.

Game For A Laugh

'Game For A Laugh', ITV's practical joke show, dominated the key Saturday evening slot for many years. Presented by arch-prankster Jeremy Beadle, the show featured members of the public doing crazy things or being set-up. The audience and presenters guffawed as their victims seethed, watching vehicles being pushed into rivers or their houses repossessed.

Barbara Woodhouse

A dog trainer who became a household name through her BBC TV series 'Training Dogs The Woodhouse Way'. She treated dog owners with such disdain that she became a cult figure. Her catchphrase 'Walkies' entered common parlance.

Dr Who

During this technological decade our favourite Timelord regenerated from Tom Baker to Peter Davison in '81, to Colin Baker in '84 and to Sylvester McCoy in '87. With so many lives used up he finally met his match... Michael Grade, the Director General of the BBC, who shelved the series in '89... but you can't keep a good time-traveller down and the brave Doctor blasted back onto our screens in 2005.

Spitting Image

'Spitting Image' broke the puppet show mould, featuring gross caricatures of people in the public eye and a fiercely satirical comedy script. With voice-overs by the likes of Rory Bremner and Alistair McGowan, the puppets acted out witty sketches. Many of those who featured on the series where actually honoured to be lampooned. The show was hugely successful and ran for 11 years, well into the Nineties.

christmas!

Band Aid release their charity record to raise more money for famine relief. In all, 'Do They Know It's Christmas?' raises over £8 million!

bomb!

On the 12th October an IRA bomb explodes at the Grand Hotel in Brighton, where Margaret Thatcher and fellow MPs are staying during the Conservative Party's annual conference. Three people are killed and many injured but the Prime Minister escapes unscathed.

1984

disasters!

Two disasters strike India: First their formidable Prime Minister, Indira Gandhi, is assassinated by her Sikh bodyguards; then a poison cloud escapes from a pesticide plant near Bhopal, leading to the deaths of some 20,000 people with many more left injured.

strike!

One of the defining events of Margaret Thatcher's tenure as British Prime Minister was her stance against the miners, who went on strike in 1984 fearing the destruction of their industry. Pitched battles were fought until the union eventually split and the mines were indeed shut. Anti-union laws were then introduced, with the balance of power back in the hands of the government.

hooray harry!

Princess Diana gives birth to her second son, Prince Harry.

and also...

- Carl Lewis wins 4 Gold Medals at the Los Angeles Olympics.
- BT, the first utility privatisation, occurs.
- Marvin Gaye, the legendary soul singer, is shot dead by his dad!
- Donald Duck is 50 years old!

1984

top flix

The Oscars:

Best Picture: Amadeus

Best Actor: F Murray Abraham (Amadeus)

Best Actress: Sally Field (Places In The Heart)

Best Of The Rest:

Beverly Hills Cop; This Is Spinal Tap; Indiana Jones And The Temple Of Doom, The Terminator.

top tv

1. Coronation Street
2. The Royal Variety Show
3. Porridge
4. Miss World
5. Bullseye

top pop

1. Do They Know It's Christmas? (Band Aid)
2. I Just Called To Say I Love You (Stevie Wonder)
3. Relax! (Frankie Goes To Hollywood)
4. Two Tribes (Frankie Goes To Hollywood)
5. Careless Whisper (George Michael)
6. Last Christmas (Wham!)
7. Hello (Lionel Richie)
8. Agadoo (Black Lace)
9. Freedom (Wham!)
10. Ghostbusters (Ray Parker Junior)

TV ~ more of the best

Kenny Everett

Where other TV comedy shows feared to tread... there went Kenny Everett! At a time of safe sit-coms he created a melting pot of outrageous characters: from Sid Snot to Cupid Stunt. His Goonish antics ranged from the scantily-dressed dancers - Hot Gossip - to his evangelizing Brother Lee Love. And, in the words of Kenny himself, it was all done "in the best possible taste!"

The Great Egg Race

A bit geeky, this series involved three teams in a race to manufacture a wacky machine out of a collection of bits and pieces and then to perform a task with an egg (get it from A to B as fast as possible, for example). The show is probably best remembered for 'mad' German inventor, Professor Heinz Wolff who was the regular judge in the earlier years of this fun and fascinating show.

Minder

'Minder's' success was due to the on screen chemistry between the spiv, Arthur Daley, played by George Cole, and his ex-boxer, ex-convict, bodyguard Terry McCann, played by Dennis Waterman. The pair were forever getting into hot water because of Daley's dodgy deals with Terry fighting their way out. The series ran from '79–'91 before Waterman bailed out to avoid being typecast! The show's theme tune, 'I Could Be So Good For You' was written and performed by Waterman.

Yes Minister

Said to be Margaret Thatcher's favourite TV programme, 'Yes Minister' was a razor-sharp sit-com set in the world of politics. It involved the adventures of the Rt. Honourable James Hacker MP, together with his Civil Service mandarin, the conniving Sir Humphrey Appleby. Appleby beguiled and manipulated the hapless Hacker until the tables were eventually turned, with hilarious consequences. The cast returned for the sequel, 'Yes Prime Minister', which was equally successful and ran until 1989.

made in america

This decade saw the mass importation of American TV. Both the BBC and ITV scored ratings hits with a raft of bought-in shows.

Cagney & Lacey

'Cagney & Lacey' was a cut above the average US cop show for it pitted two women against New York's hoodlums and the sexist NYPD. After an initial TV film and series with different actresses playing the roles, Sharon Gless eventually became the regular Cagney whilst Tyne Daly played the married, sensitive Mary Beth Lacey. The series ran throughout the decade, picking up a shelf-full of awards as a hard-hitting police drama.

Dallas

Based in the oil fields of Texas ~ where every man seemed to walk around in a ten-gallon hat and cowboy boots, and where the women were beautiful, bitchy and boozy ~ 'Dallas' became a huge success. It centred round the oil-rich Ewing family of Southfork with eldest son JR Ewing proving to be, arguably, one of television's greatest villains. When an unknown assailant tried to kill JR it was headline stuff and bookies laid odds on who pulled the trigger. 'Dallas' was by far the top US soap with copycats and spin-offs such as 'Dynasty' and 'Knots Landing' never reaching the same heights.

The A Team

"In 1972 a crack commando unit was sent to prison by a military court for a crime they didn't commit. These men promptly escaped from a maximum security stockade to the Los Angeles underground. Today, still wanted by the government, they survive as soldiers of fortune. If you have a problem, if no one else can help, and if you can find them, maybe you can hire the A-Team." So began this romp of a series which featured a group of Vietnam veterans who acted as latterday Robin Hoods helping the victims of injustice. Team members included Hannibal Smith, Mad Murdoch, BA (Bad Attitiude) Baracus and Faceman. The series was a huge hit on both sides of the Atlantic and even starred Boy George in one episode.

Other notable favourites

Miami Vice; Moonlighting; Magnum PI; Knight Rider; Buck Rogers; Battlestar Galactica; The Colbys; Cheers, Taxi.

science & technology

Stealth Bombers

A possible explanation for all those UFO sightings in America was revealed in 1988! The Lockheed F117A Nighthawk was America's first stealth weapon. The angular nature of the 'flying wing' and the radar-absorbing material with which it was made allowed the plane to fly virtually undetected into enemy airspace. The Nighthawk could carry a payload of two 2000lb bombs.

Smallpox

The World Heath Authority announced in 1980 that a scourge of mankind, the smallpox virus, had at last been defeated. A mass vaccination campaign which had been launched in the mid-Sixties had successfully slowed and eventually eradicated the killer bug. No case of smallpox has since been detected.

The Space Shuttle

In 1981 NASA's reusable space craft, the Space Shuttle, had its maiden flight. The first shuttle, Columbia, had taken longer to design and build than the entire Apollo project which took man on the Moon. There were a total of five shuttle orbiters built. Tragically, Challenger exploded soon after launch in 1986 and Columbia broke up on re-entry in 2003; on each occasion all 7 crew perished.

The PC

In 1981, IBM launched its first serious Personal Computer. The market leaders with DOS computers, IBM were taken aback when Apple launched the first Macintosh with a mouse and menus so they asked a company to create an add-on to MS-DOS with an interface similar to the Mac's. That company was Microsoft & hence 'Windows' was born.

Mir

Mir (which means both 'world' and 'peace' in Russian) was a highly successful Soviet space station. Mir was assembled in space over a period of ten years and was the home to Soviet and international astronauts throughout this period.

The Cosmonauts broke many endurance records whilst inhabiting the orbiting scientific laboratory. In 2001, Mir came to the end of its life, and was deliberately allowed to drop out of its orbit and burn up in the Earth's atmosphere.

The Ozone Layer

1985 saw the announcement that a hole had been detected in the ozone layer of the atmosphere over Antarctica.

Ozone is critical to the planet's well-being as it filters out harmful UV radiation. There were many arguments as to whether this was natural or man-made. Chlorofluorocarbons, or CFCs, were implicated due to their widespread use in fridges and aerosols. The discovery of the 'hole' gave rise to alternatives to CFCs and alerted the non-scientific world to the effect of Man's actions on the planet.

DNA

1987 saw the first criminal convicted following analysis of DNA left at the scene of a crime. The new science of 'genetic fingerprinting' was developed by Dr. Alec Jeffreys of Leicester University.

HIV AIDS

Acquired Immune Deficiency Syndrome or Aids is the name for a collection of symptoms and infections in humans resulting from damage to the immune system caused by infection by the human immunodeficiency virus (HIV). AIDS was discovered in 1981 in the US after a spate of fatal illnesses in the gay community. Originally dubbed GRID - Gay-Related Immune Deficiency - it was soon determined that heterosexuals were also at risk. The term AIDS - where A stands for Aquired - was promptly adopted. The link between AIDS and the Human Immunodeficiency Virus was revealed by Dr. Luc Montagnier in 1983.

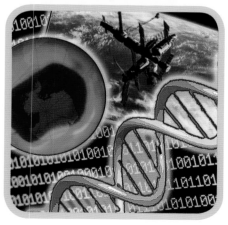

bombing

The Greenpeace ship Rainbow Warrior, protesting against French nuclear tests, is blown up in Auckland by French agents. One crew member is killed.

1985

c5 anyone?

Sir Clive Sinclair launches his latest invention ~ a battery operated tricycle called the C5. It has a range of 32 km (20 miles), costs £399 and is made by Hoover. Ill-conceived, the C5 is ridiculed as dangerous and has a short life. Plans for a whole series of electric cars are canned.

disasters

There were two major football disasters in '85: In the first, a small fire starts in the corner of the Bradford City ground. Within minutes the stands go up in flames and 52 fans lose their lives. Then at the European Cup Final at the Heysel Stadium in Brussels, fighting between Liverpool and Juventus fans sees 41 Italian and Belgian supporters killed as a wall and crash barrier collapse. Astonishingly, the match goes ahead and Juventus win.

live aid

Following the success of their charity record, Bob Geldof and Midge Ure organise the Live Aid concert at Wembley Stadium and, simultaneously, at Philadelphia's JFK Stadium. Lasting 12 hours, the marathon event is watched by 1.5 billion people around the world. Over £40 million is raised for famine relief in Ethiopia.

and also...

- Coca-Cola launch a new, sweeter recipe. It's a disaster!
- Gary Kasparov becomes the youngest World Chess Champion.
- The wreck of the Titanic is discovered.
- The Church of England approves the ordination of women.

1985

top flix

The Oscars:

Best Picture: Out Of Africa

Best Actor: William Hurt (Kiss Of The Spider Woman)

Best Actress: Geraldine Page (The Trip To Bountiful)

Best Of The Rest:

Back To The Future; Witness; Rambo; Mask, The Color Purple.

top tv

1. EastEnders
2. Coronation Street
3. Wish You Were Here
4. Open All Hours
5. Last Of The Summer Wine

top pop

1. The Power Of Love (Jennifer Rush)
2. I Know Him So Well (Elaine Page / Barbara Dickson)
3. Into The Groove (Madonna)
4. 19 (Paul Hardcastle)
5. Frankie (Sister Sledge)
6. Dancing In The Streets (David Bowie / Mick Jagger)
7. Move Closer (Phyllis Nelson)
8. Take On Me (A-ha)
9. A Good Heart (Feargal Sharkey)
10. I Want To Know What Love Is (Foreigner)

films

The Shining

Released in 1980, this classic horror film was based upon the Steven King novel of the same name. Starring Jack Nicholson as tormented writer, Jack Torrance, and Shelley Duvall as his wife Wendy, it features one of the most famous scenes of all time in which Jack hacks his way through a door with an axe, and shouts "Here's Johnny!" through a hole.

Raiders Of The Lost Ark

Tom Selleck was cast in the role of Indiana Jones, but turned it down due to his heavy shooting schedule for the TV show 'Magnum'. Spielberg convinced Lucas to pick Harrison Ford and the rest is history! The plot involves foiling the Nazis in their attempt to find the fabled Ark of the Covenant ~ any army marching into battle with it becomes invincible. 'Raiders' remains one of the highest-grossing films of all time and is arguably one of the greatest action/adventure films ever made.

Ghostbusters

"Who ya gonna call?!" This paranormal hit-squad burst onto the silver screen in 1984. Great writing, fantastic casting, tongue-in-cheek humour and a fun story made this film an instant box-office hit.

Back To The Future

This 1985 film follows the adventures of Marty McFly and his eccentric scientist friend, Doc Brown, who has discovered the secret to time-travel. Doc builds a time-machine out of a stainless steel DeLorean sports car powered by plutonium from dubious sources. During a test, terrorists turn up to claim the plutonium. After seeing Doc shot dead, Marty jumps in the DeLorean and disappears back to 1955. He succeeds in meeting a young Doc Brown and convinces him to help but unfortunately also meets his own teenage mother - who promptly falls for him! Marty must get his mum and dad to fall in love or else risk non-existance whilst returning to 1985 in time to save Doc's life! The first of a successful trilogy, 'Back To The Future' was a massive box-office hit.

Top Gun

Question: What do you get if you blend dodgy acting, a cheesy script, a sickly-sweet theme song with a large helping of good ol' American 'save-the-world' patriotism? Answer: A guaranteed box office success! Released in 1986, Top Gun has since become something of a cult film. Whatever your opinion about it, it does have some fine flying sequences - although the 'baddies' fly MiG 28s - a plane which has never existed!

E.T. - The Extra-Terrestrial

Grossing an astonishing $793 million, E.T. remains arguably Spielberg's best work. A classic fairytale story, loveable characters, great special effects and a wonderful musical score all combined to make this a firm family favourite - then and now. The film was even screened at the United Nations and Spielberg received the U.N. Peace Medal. Urban legend has it that the story is based loosely upon a true happening and that during a private screening, President Reagan told Spielberg that the public "would never know how true this was"! E.T. lost out in the Best Picture Oscar to worthy 'Ghandi'.

Chariots Of Fire

Released in 1981, 'Chariots Of Fire' is based upon the true story of British athletes preparing for and competing in the 1924 Summer Olympics. Now, it probably remains most famous for its beach running scene overlaid with the iconic Vangelis theme tune.

Who Framed Roger Rabbit?

Staring Bob Hoskins, this film was groundbreaking in its combination of live action and animation. It was one of the most expensive films of the decade with a budget of some $70 million. It proved a sound investment though, bringing home $150 million through the box office.

Other films of the decade:

American Gigolo; Rain Man; Gandhi; Dirty Dancing; Flashdance; Fatal Attraction; The Terminator; The Blues Brothers; Wall Street; An American Werewolf In London; Conan The Barbarian; Blade Runner; Scarface; Beverly Hills Cop; Rambo; This Is Spinal Tap; Out Of Africa; A Nightmare On Elm Street; Platoon; When Harry Met Sally; Arthur; The Untouchables; Batman; Tootsie, Driving Miss Daisy.

chernobyl

The Soviets announce, four days after the event, that the Chernobyl nuclear power station in the Ukraine is on fire. Offers of help are refused. The radiation pollutes the atmosphere affecting people, livestock and land across Europe making it the world's worst nuclear accident to date.

1986

challenger

The US space shuttle Challenger explodes only 72 seconds after take-off, killing all seven astronauts on board. The cause appears to be icicles which covered the shuttle craft on the morning of the launch. An investigation begins into the cause of the explosion.

wedding

Prince Andrew weds Sarah Ferguson at Westminster Abbey.

chunnel

The UK and France announce that a Channel Tunnel will be built before 1993 linking the two nations.

hand of god

Maradonna effectively puts England out of the World Cup when he out-jumps Peter Shilton and fists a ball past him into the net. The referee misses the illegal move and Argentina go on to win the match 2-1.

quins

The first test-tube quintuplets are born at University College Hospital, London. Linda and Bruce Jacobssen now have five sons, Alan, Brett, Edward, Dougal and Connor!

and also...

- America bombs Libya.
- Ian Botham is banned from cricket after smoking dope.
- Hampton Court Palace is badly damaged after a fire.
- Prince Charles admits he talks to plants!

1986

top flix

The Oscars:

Best Picture: Platoon

Best Actor: Paul Newman (The Color Of Money)

Best Actress: Marlee Martin (Children Of A Lesser God)

Best Of The Rest:

Top Gun; Down And Out In Beverly Hills; Ruthless, Aliens.

top pop

1. Don't Leave Me This Way (The Communards)
2. Every Loser Wins (Nick Berry)
3. I Want To Wake Up With You (Boris Gardiner)
4. Living Doll (Cliff Richard & The Young Ones)
5. Chain Reaction (Diana Ross)
6. Lady In Red (Chris De Burgh)
7. When The Going Gets Tough (Billy Ocean)
8. Take My Breath Away (Berlin)
9. Papa Don't Preach (Madonna)
10. So Macho (Sinitta)

top tv

1. EastEnders
2. Just Good Friends
3. Only Fools And Horses
4. Coronation Street
5. Royal Wedding

people

John Lennon

On the 9th December 1980 ex-Beatle John Lennon was shot dead outside the Dakota apartment building in New York where he lived with his wife Yoko Ono. His assassin, Mark Chapman, had been stalking the singer for several days and was even photographed earlier in the day whilst getting an autograph from Lennon.

Margaret Thatcher

Britain's first woman Prime Minister declared on her election day that "Where there is discord may we bring harmony... where there is despair may we bring hope". The '80s became the 'Thatcherite' decade in which the Iron Lady gained an international reputation for sticking to her principles. She was loved and loathed in equal measure: In the south-east, which saw huge economic growth, she was loved; In the north, which suffered as it lost its manufacturing and heavy industry, she was a figure of hate. She won re-election in 1983 thanks in part to the patriotism surrounding the Falklands War and also due to a divided Labour Party. She won again in 1987 with a 101 seat majority, securing her place as Britain's longest serving PM since Lord Liverpool in 1827! Even hard-edged socialists admitted a grudging respect for the single-mindedness with which she stuck to her guns. Ironically, it was this stubbornness which ultimately led to her downfall. In 1990, opposition to policies on local government taxation and a sharp downturn in the economy caused deep divisions in her party. Finally voted out of office in a bitter power struggle, she remains one of the most influential Prime Ministers of all time.

Ronald Reagan

Ronald Reagan was a B-movie actor who lived the American Dream, becoming State Governor of California and eventually President of the United States. Reagan survived an assassination attempt in 1981. He had a particularly close relationship with Margaret Thatcher and, through his ratcheting up of the arms race, is attributed with forcing the Soviet Union to the negotiating table and bringing about an end to the Cold War.

Mikhail Gorbachev

Without doubt, Mikhail Gorbachev changed the course of Russian history. As soon as he was appointed as General Secretary of the Communist Party he introduced two radical policies… 'perestroika' (which means restructuring) and 'glasnost' (openness). His willingness to talk about nuclear disarmament with the US led to a thawing of the Cold War but the restructuring of the Soviet economy brought much hardship and the gradual break-up of the Soviet Union.

Lech Walesa

This ship-building Trade Unionist took on the Polish Communist Government and, through his Solidarity movement, went on to be the first democratically elected President in Eastern Europe.

Bob Geldof

Geldof had experienced personal success during the years of Punk with his band 'The Boomtown Rats'. During the mid-Eighties, when his music career was in decline, he was moved by the tragedy of the Ethiopian famine and put his energies into fund-raising. Together with Midge Ure, he penned and recorded a charity single 'Do They Know It's Christmas?'. Its success led to a live concert, Live Aid, which raised millions for Africa and brought him international acclaim.

Salman Rushdie

The publishing of 'The Satanic Verses' in 1988 upset the world's muslim community and the President of Iran, Ayatollah Khomeini, issued a 'fatwah' calling for the author's death. Rushdie was to live in hiding until the late '90s.

Rock Hudson

The male heart-throb, Rock Hudson, died of AIDS, the first public figure to die of the disease in America. A popular star who usually played 'macho' roles, he was secretly gay.

toys & games

Smurfs

These blue-coloured models caused a collecting frenzy after Dutch singer Father Abraham released the first Smurf single at the end of the '70s; it was a worldwide hit. By the '80s, toys and figurines filled the toyshops and school children started collecting the tiny blue coloured characters. In 1981, Hanna & Barbera created a cartoon series where the characters of 'Jokey', 'Greedy' and 'Brainy Smurf' sought advice from 'Papa Smurf'; 'Smurfette' was the only female member of the blue clan.

Rubik's Cube

This icon of the '80s was invented by Erno Rubik (a Hungarian sculptor and Professor of Architecture) in 1975 but only 'discovered' in 1980. The Cube went into mass-production, spawning a craze in which the masses cracked their knuckles in a race to rearrange the puzzle - ultimately the fastest time in which to complete it dropped to 16.5 seconds! A later version, called 'Rubik's Revenge', had four rows of four squares instead of the standard three. Selling over 100 million units worldwide, it's generally accepted to be the best-selling toy ever!

Cabbage Patch Kids

These dolls created such a craze that people queued up in toy shops just to get their hands on one. No two dolls were alike: eye, hair colour, clothes and features all varied. The brain-child of Xavier Roberts, the dolls were made in a factory which had formerly been a medical clinic: re-named 'Babyland General Hospital', each doll came complete with its own 'birth certificate'. By 1982 the dolls had evolved into the 'Cabbage Patch Kids' and a fad was born. In 1984, 20 million dolls were bought, and, by 1999, 95 million had been sold!

My Little Pony

The first vinyl toy version was mass-produced in 1982. Brightly coloured with long flowing manes and tails, these collectible figurines quickly became an obsession with young girls. A TV series and a movie based on the characters were also made.

Care Bears

First appearing on greeting cards in 1981, they evolved into plush teddy bears in 1983. Each Care Bear came in a different colour and had a special design on its tummy which, it was claimed, represented its 'personality'.

Trivial Pursuit

Trivial Pursuit became the best-selling board game of 1984 and went on to sell over 30 million world-wide in 18 languages and 32 countries.

Teddy Ruxpin

Teddy Ruxpin was first produced in 1985. He could move his mouth and eyes as he read stories via a cassette player built into his back. You could also buy a companion toy called Grubby which would plug into Ruxpin, allowing the two limited interaction with each other.

BMX Bikes

BMX stood for Bicycle Motocross and the BMX Burner made by Raleigh became the action bike of 1982. Kids were able to perform stunt tricks and wheelies and ride over rough terrain as never before. It was more akin to scramble biking without the motor, but kids had to wear protective helmets & knee/arm pads all the same.

Transformers

First appearing in the USA in 1984, Transformers were THE toy to have on most boys' Christmas lists. The line was divided into two: the Evil Decepticons and the Heroic Autobots. They were mostly trucks, cars and planes which could convert into a robotic action figure. As the tagline put it, they were 'robots in disguise'!

black monday

20th October sees an unprecedented crash on the Wall Street Stock Exchange. After months of rising share values throughout the world the bubble eventually bursts. In the US $500 billion is wiped of the values of companies within a day!

1987

terry waite

Westerners in Beirut, Lebanon, are frequently kidnapped by the warring parties. Terry Waite, the Archbishop of Canterbury's Special Envoy, is in Beirut negotiating the release of hostages when he, himself, is abducted. He spends 4 years incarcerated.

hurricane?

The South of England is hit by hurricane winds of up to 176 km/h (110 mph) after weather forecasters fail to predict the freak storm. Michael Fish, the BBC weather forecaster, famously states that there is "no need to worry". Millions of pounds of damage is caused by the winds.

dark days

In a torrid year, Britain suffers four major disasters. The Herald Of Free Enterprise ferry capsizes near Zeebrugge, Holland; a huge blaze at London's King's Cross tube station claims 30 lives; Michael Ryan shoots dead 16 people in Hungerford during a killing spree and the IRA bomb a Remembrance Service at Enniskillen, Northern Ireland, murdering 11 people.

and also...

- Andy Warhol, the artist and film-maker, dies aged 57.
- Margaret Thatcher is elected for a third term as Prime Minister!
- The Iran-Contra scandal rocks America.
- Van Gogh's 'Irises' sells for £53.9 million.
- Matthias Rust, a 19 year-old West German flies a small plane through Soviet air defences and lands in Moscow's Red Square!

top flix

The Oscars:
Best Picture:
The Last Emperor
Best Actor: Michael Douglas (Wall Street)
Best Actress: Cher (Moonstruck)
Best Of The Rest:
The China Syndrome; Fatal Attraction; Predator; Dirty Dancing; Beverly Hills Cop II; The Running Man, The Untouchables.

top pop

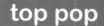

1. Never Gonna Give You Up (Rick Astley)
2. Nothing's Gonna Stop Us Now (Starship)
3. I Wanna Dance With Somebody (Whitney Houston)
4. You Win Again (Bee Gees)
5. China In Your Hand (T'Pau)
6. Respectable (Mel & Kim)
7. Stand By Me (Ben E. King)
8. It's A Sin (Pet Shop Boys)
9. Pump Up The Volume (M/A/R/R/S)
10. Star Trekkin' (The Firm)

top tv

1. EastEnders
2. Coronation Street
3. A Question Of Sport
4. Royal It's A Knockout
5. Children In Need

sport

Moscow Olympics

Held in 1980, the Moscow Olympics is remembered for the fact that America and many European countries boycotted the Games. The Soviet invasion and occupation of Afghanistan forced the international community to act and a mass boycott resulted. Of all the European countries only Britain attended. The Games were notable for the number of World Records achieved and the battle between middle-distance runners Sebastian Coe and Steve Ovett.

Tennis

The Eighties threw up a number of great players in the world of tennis. Björn Borg had dominated the sport throughout the late Seventies but his grip on the Wimbledon Trophy was finally loosened by a precocious youngster - John McEnroe. Borg had won five consecutive Wimbledon titles but the young pretender took his crown in 1981. Martina Navratilova dominated the women's game, battling other greats that included Chris Evert, Evonne Goolagong/Crawley and Steffi Graf. In 1985, Boris Becker burst onto the scene to become the only unseeded player to win the Men's Singles at Wimbledon until Goran Ivanisevic in 2001.

World Cups

There were, of course, two World Cups during the Eighties, held in Spain in 1982 and Mexico in 1986. Italy won in Spain, beating West Germany 3-1 in the Final. England failed to get beyond the group stages. In Mexico, England faced Argentina in the Quarter-finals. They lost to the eventual champions but the game was marred by Maradonna's cynical 'Hand of God' goal…a deliberate handball flicked past Shilton and into the England net!

Torvill & Dean

Torvill and Dean, the most famous ice dancers of their generation, were British, European, and Olympic champions.

At the Winter Olympics in 1984 their performance, set to Ravel's 'Bolero', made them the highest-scoring skaters of all time. They were awarded 12 'sixes' for the final free dance section and a perfect 9 'sixes' in the artistic interpretation category.

Tyson

A young and ferocious heavyweight burst into the boxing arena in the late Eighties. Mike Tyson was only 20 years old when he became the youngest Heavyweight World Champion of all time in 1986. A vicious fighter with a devastating punch, he dominated the fight scene until his own personal demons got the better of him.

lockerbie

A Pan Am Boeing 747, en route to New York, explodes shortly after take-off with the debris falling on the Scottish town of Lockerbie. All 259 passengers and crew perish together with 11 residents on the ground. A bomb is suspected and eventually Libya is blamed for the crime.

disaster

The oil platform Piper Alpha explodes and 167 riggers lose their lives.

starstruck

Former Reagan right-hand man and namesake, Donald Regan, claims that the US President regularly consults his wife's astrologer before making major decisions. The White House dismisses the claims but the masses believe them!

1988

red noses

Comic Relief is launched to raise money for famine relief in Africa. The money is raised through sponsored events by members of the public and a six-hour comedy telethon screened on the BBC. The selling of plastic red noses helps to reach the donations target.

party!

The joining of the Liberal and SDP parties brings about a new political party ~ The Social & Liberal Democrats.

drinking!

The UK pub licensing hours are extended so that pubs can now stay open from 11am to 11pm on weekdays.

and also...

- The Shroud Of Turin is (perhaps!) proved to be medieval fake.
- Three trains collide at Clapham Junction. Thirty five passengers are killed.
- The dark blue British passport is replaced by a red EC-format passport.

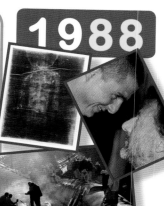

1988

top flix

The Oscars:

Best Picture: Rain Man

Best Actor: Dustin Hoffman (Rain Man)

Best Actress: Jodie Foster (The Accused)

Best Of The Rest:

Big; The Last Temptation Of Christ; Dangerous Liaisons; Who Framed Roger Rabbit?, Twins.

top tv

1. EastEnders
2. Bread
3. Neighbours
4. Coronation Street
5. Last Of The Summer Wine

top pop

1. Mistletoe And Wine (Cliff Richard)
2. The Only Way Is Up (Yazz & The Plastic Population)
3. I Should Be So Lucky (Kylie Minogue)
4. Especially For You (Kylie Minogue & Jason Donovan)
5. I Think We're Alone Now (Tiffany)
6. Nothing's Gonna Change My Love For You (Glenn Medeiros)
7. A Groovy Kind Of Love (Phil Collins)
8. With A Little Help From My Friends (Wet Wet Wet)
9. He Ain't Heavy He's My Brother (The Hollies)
10. Teardrops (Womack & Womack)

on the move

New Trains

This decade saw the launch of the TGV, the French high-speed train. Running from Paris to Lyon in 2 hours 40 minutes it averaged 133 mph with a maximum speed of 168 mph. The UK's answer to the TGV was the APT or Advanced Passenger Train. To achieve high speed on existing track it used a tilting mechanism - but unfortunately this made passengers sick and the train proved unreliable.

Classic Cars

The Volkswagen Golf GTI was launched in the Seventies but is essentially an Eighties icon. The Golf was the first successful front wheel drive hatchback and the GTI version virtually created the hot hatch genre overnight.

Hot on the heels of the Golf GTI came another hot hatch, the mid-engined Renault 5. Designed for rallying, there was also a road-going version: although marketed under the Renault 5 badge it barely resembled the volume model and had looks that boy-racers would die for! Although the British car industry was in the doldrums, Austin Rover was not to be outdone, producing the MG Metro 6RW. Built for the rallying circuit, the competition version of the Metro bore only a passing resemblance to the production car. A two-seater, 4WD, mid-engined vehicle, the 6R4 was unusual insomuch as it wasn't turbo-charged! The car's life was short-lived, achieving a creditable third place behind Lancia's Deltas in the '85 RAC Rally. Supercars were banned from rallying later that year following a number of fatal accidents.

Lotus had the habit of designing and manufacturing highly desirable (though oft-unreliable) sports cars. Amongst the most successful was the Lotus Esprit, which was manufactured for almost thirty years. The wedge-shaped Esprit Turbo was launched in 1980 and proved a huge success. The car appeared in the 1981 James Bond film 'For Your Eyes Only', replacing the Aston Martins with another truly-British performance car.

With a top speed of almost 200mph, the Porsche 959 was lauded as the most advanced road-going sports car ever built. Some 300 were constructed from 1986–1988 but with such a high price tag that only the super-rich could afford them - Bill Gates, for example!

Ford's XR2 and XR3i were boy-racer hot-hatches based on the Fiesta and the Escort respectively. Popular with car thieves and joy-riders, they became expensive to insure and were withdrawn in the early 1990s.

John DeLorean received Government funding to produce the stainless-steel skinned, gull-winged DeLorean DMC-12 based upon the Lotus Esprit. Built for the US market in an all-new factory in Northern Ireland, only 9,000 were ever made - although one famously appeared in 'Back To The Future'. The company went bust in 1982. DeLorean himself was arrested and accused of drug trafficking but was ultimately cleared of all charges.

'80s buzzwords

SHOPAHOLIC
A person who is addicted to shopping.

BODY-POPPING
Jerky body movements made whilst break-dancing.

CHANNEL SURFER
Someone who flicks constantly between TV channels using a remote control.

MULTI-TASKING
The uncanny ability of doing more than one thing at a time.

BONK
Common vernacular for 'having sex'.

SMILEY
The yellow smiley face icon adopted by Acid House ravers.

TOY BOY
A young male lover adorning a much older woman.

BACK-UP
To protect data on a computer by regularly copying to a disc or remote hard drive.

BUM BAG
A small vinyl or leather pouch with a belt that is worn around the waist. Known, amusingly, as a 'fanny pack' in the USA.

LOONY LEFT
This was a term developed by the media to describe people or organisations with far-left politics, especially a number of Labour controlled inner-city councils, whose actions were considered crackpot by the popular press.

CAR BOOT SALE
A large jumble sale where the goods are displayed from the back of a car.

"don't quote me"

Del Boy:
"Luvley Jubbly"
(David Jason plays Del Boy in TV sitcom "Only Fools and Horses")

Dan Quayle:
"I took Latin in school"
(A comment made by Dan Quayle whilst visiting Latin America)

On TV's Quiz Show: 'BLOCKBUSTERS'
'I'll have a 'P' please Bob!'

Margaret Thatcher:
"A world without nuclear weapons would be less stable and more dangerous for all of us."

George Bush Snr.
"Read my lips - no new taxes" (said shortly before new taxes were indeed introduced)

Margaret Thatcher:
"The lady's not for turning"

Ronald Reagan:
"I have left orders to be awakened at any time in case of national emergency, even if I'm in a cabinet meeting."

Margaret Thatcher:
"There are still people in my party who believe in consensus politics. I regard them as Quislings, as traitors... I mean it!"

Frankie Goes to Hollywood
"Frankie says RELAX"

Ronald Reagan:
"Today we did what we had to do. They counted on America to be passive. They counted wrong."
(After US warplanes attacked Libya in retaliation for bombing a discotheque in East Berlin frequented by US military personnel.)

Paul McCartney:
"The older generation make marijuana out to be a terrible thing.... We are all on drugs, cigarettes, whisky and wild women."

satanic

Author Salman Rushdie's new book 'The Satanic Verses' causes public outcry from Muslim communities. They claim the book is blasphemous and demonstrate their anger by burning the book in front of television news crews.

tiananmen

China's fledgling pro-democracy movement mounts protests in Beijing's Tiananmen Square. There is a brutal clamp-down by the authorities and the People's Army kills an estimated 3,000 protesters whilst injuring 10,000 more.

Perhaps the most poignant image is that of a solitary, still unknown, man standing passively yet defiantly before a long column of advancing People's Army tanks.

1989

berlin wall

1989 sees the fall of the most potent symbol of the East-West divide. East Germany opens up its border checkpoints as its regime goes into meltdown. East and West Germans band together to destroy the hated Berlin Wall. Throughout Europe Communist regimes collapse as Soviet authority withers and fades. Reunification of Germany soon follows.

guildford

In 1975 four Irishmen are convicted and given long prison sentences for the Guildford pub bombings. 1989 sees the case dismissed on appeal and the men released. It is one of Britain's great miscarriages of justice as the court of appeal concludes that confessions had been fabricated.

tragedy

1989

1989 sees yet another football tragedy when 94 football fans die in a crush at Hillsborough, the home of Nottingham Forest. Too many supporters are allowed to enter the ground and fans are crushed against the fences provided to protect the pitch.

top flix

The Oscars:
Best Picture:
Driving Miss Daisy
Best Actor:
Daniel Day-Lewis
(My Left Foot)
Best Actress:
Jessica Tandy
(Driving Miss Daisy)
Best Of The Rest:
Batman; Indiana Jones And The Last Crusade; Ghostbusters II; Sex Lies & Video Tape, When Harry Met Sally.

top tv

1. Coronation Street
2. EastEnders
3. Neighbours
4. Only Fools And Horses
5. Tyson v Bruno Title Fight

top pop

1. Ride On Time (Black Box)
2. Swing The Mood (Jive Bunny & The Mastermixers)
3. Eternal Flame (The Bangles)
4. Too Many Broken Hearts (Jason Donovan)
5. Back To Life (Soul II Soul)
6. Something's Gotten Hold Of My Heart (Almond/Pitney)
7. That's What I Like (Jive Bunny & The Mastermixers)
8. Pump Up The Jam (Technotronic)
9. Do They Know It's Christmas? (Band Aid II)
10. Like A Prayer (Madonna)

and also...

• The supertanker Exxon Valdez hits a reef spilling an oil slick covering 1300 square km.

• A coup in Romania leads to the execution of dictator Nicolae Ceausescu and his wife.

• Ayatollah Khomeini, spiritual leader of Iran, is buried. Amidst scenes of mass hysteria his coffin is up-turned in the crowd.

• The Soviets admit defeat and withdraw from Afghanistan.

so there you have it!

We have reached the end of a frantic decade of new developments and staggering changes! We've seen how the Eighties saw a rapid expansion in many areas which now define the modern age, from personal computers to video games; the compact disc to the mobile phone! The decade was one of contrasts: whilst personal fortunes were being made in the world's market economies, the nation was also developing a social conscience with environmental and green issues coming to the fore.

CND protested against the deployment of Cruise Missiles and the disaster at Chernobyl focused the world's attention like never before.

The 'Me Decade' will always be remembered for the 'haves' and the 'have nots', the pursuit of personal wealth and fulfilment at the expense of the less fortunate; but it should also, surely, be remembered for the exceptional international events that it witnessed… the collapse of Communism; the fall of the Berlin Wall; the seeds of change in China and the beginning of the end of apartheid in South Africa. Truly a period of dramatic change… and deely-boppers too!

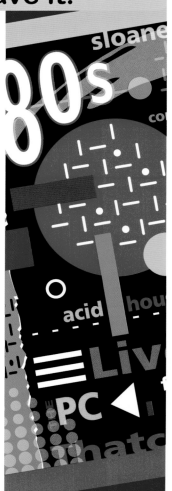

scoring the cd game

The grid below is for you to keep a running total of each player or team's score as you play the games on the CD.

Enter the player or team's name or initials at the head of each double column with a pencil.

Having answered and marked questions, enter the total for the round on the left and keep a running total on the right.

The winner will have the greatest overall total once all 9 tracks in the game have been played.

TEAMS>	1		2		3		4	
Track 1								
Track 2								
Track 3								
Track 4								
Track 5								
Track 6								
Track 7								
Track 8								
Track 9								
TOTAL>								

Rub out the score sheet to play again or download fresh sheets from:
www.cheatwell.com > downloads > Spot the Intro score sheets

Game 1 Answers (tracks 1-9)

- **Spot The Intro: Track 1**
1) Come On Eileen - Dexy's Midnight Runners, 1982
2) I Should Be So Lucky - Kylie Minogue, 1989
3) Arthur's Theme - Christopher Cross, 1981
4) Manic Monday - Bangles, 1986
5) All The Love In The World - Dionne Warwick, 1982
- **Music: Track 2**
1) Simple Minds
2) OMD (Orchestral Manoeuvres In The Dark)
3) Flash Gordon
4) Making Your Mind Up
5) The Vapors
- **Spot The Intro: Track 3**
1) Tell Her About It - Billy Joel, 1983
2) Save A Prayer - Duran Duran, 1982
3) Rapture - Blondie, 1981
4) Easy Lover - Phil Collins and Philip Bailey, 1985
5) Every Breath You Take - The Police, 1983
- **TV & Film: Track 4**
1) Indiana Jones
2) EastEnders
3) The Shining
4) Countdown
5) 8
- **Spot The Intro: Track 5**
1) Starmaker - Kids From Fame, 1982
2) Lady In Red - Chris De Burgh, 1986
3) Dead Ringer For Love - Meatloaf, 1981
4) Bette Davis Eyes - Kim Carnes, 1981
5) Heaven Is A Place On Earth - Belinda Carlisle, 1987
- **Fads & Fashions: Track 6**
1) David & Elizabeth Emmanuel
2) The ra ra skirt
3) Acid House
4) Garfield
5) Rubik's Cube
- **Spot The Intro: Track 7**
1) Sweet Dreams (Are Made Of This) - Eurythmics, 1983
2) Don't Leave Me This Way - Communards, 1986
3) Let's Groove - Earth Wind And Fire, 1981
4) Here I Go Again - Whitesnake, 1982
5) It's Raining Men - The Weather Girls, 1984
- **Events: Track 8**
1) The Iron Lady
2) The half penny
3) Indira Gandhi
4) Boris Becker
5) Galtieri

- **Spot The Intro: Track 9**
1) Girls On Film - Duran Duran, 1981
2) Vienna - Ultravox, 1981
3) Young At Heart - Bluebells, 1984
4) Special Brew - Bad Manners, 1980
5) The Bitterest Pill (I Ever Had To Swallow) - The Jam, 1982

Game 2 Answers (tracks 10-18)

- **Spot The Intro: Track 10**
1) More Than I Can Say - Leo Sayer, 1980
2) Poison Arrow - ABC, 1982
3) White Wedding - Billy Idol, 1985
4) Only You - Yazoo 1982
5) Word Up - Cameo, 1986
- **Music: Track 11**
1) The Coconuts
2) Adam Ant
3) Ska
4) The Weather Girls
5) Michael Jackson
- **Spot The Intro: Track 12**
1) Power Of Love - Frankie Goes To Hollywood, 1984
2) Like A Virgin - Madonna, 1984
3) Thriller - Michael Jackson, 1983
4) Karma Chameleon - Culture Club, 1983
5) Sledgehammer - Peter Gabriel, 1986
- **TV & Film: Track 13**
1) Kristin, his sister-in-law and mistress
2) Blade Runner
3) Fame
4) Sylvester Stallone
5) 1981
- **Spot The Intro: Track 14**
1) Reet Petite - Jackie Wilson, 1986
2) Orinoco Flow - Enya, 1988
3) Three Little Birds, Bob Marley, 1980
4) Uptown Girl - Billy Joel, 1983
5) Woman - John Lennon, 1981
- **Fads & Fashions: Track 15**
1) The C5 electric vehicle
2) The head
3) Disc camera
4) Nicoret, nicotine chewing gum
5) Body popping
- **Spot The Intro: Track 16**
1) All Around The World - Lisa Stansfield, 1989
2) A Different Corner - George Michael, 1986
3) The Tide Is High - Blondie, 1980
4) Gloria - Laura Branigan, 1982
5) Belfast Child - Simple Minds, 1989

- **Events: Track 17**
1) Ayatollah Khomeini
2) Bhopal
3) Lech Walesa
4) Arthur Scargill
5) Daley Thompson
- **Spot The Intro: Track 18**
1) Holiday - Madonna, 1984
2) Ashes To Ashes - David Bowie, 1980
3) Run To You - Bryan Adams, 1985
4) Walk Like An Egyptian - Bangles, 1986
5) Perfect - Fairground Attraction, 1988

Game 3 Answers (tracks 19-27)

- **Spot The Intro: Track 19**
1) I Won't Let The Sun Go Down On Me - Nik Kershaw, 1984
2) Wherever I Lay My Hat - Paul Young, 1983
3) Ay Ay Ay Ay Moosey - Modern Romance, 1981
4) I Wanna Wake Up With You - Boris Gardener, 1986
5) In The Air Tonight - Phil Collins, 1981
- **Music: Track 20**
1) Toto
2) Haircut 100
3) Hissing Sid's
4) 1988
5) Clannad
- **Spot The Intro: Track 21**
1) If You Don't Know Me By Now - Simply Red, 1989
2) Under Pressure - Queen & David Bowie, 1981
3) Purple Rain - Prince, 1984
4) Hands Up - Ottawan, 1981
5) Hold Me Now - Thompson Twins, 1983
- **TV & Film: Track 22**
1) The Color Purple
2) Oprah Winfrey
3) The Woman In Red
4) Alien Life Form
5) Educating Rita
- **Spot The Intro: Track 23**
1) Eye Of The Tiger - Survivor, 1982
2) True - Spandau Ballet, 1983
3) Englishman In New York - Sting, 1988
4) Thorn In My Side - Eurythmics, 1986
5) Heartbreaker - Dionne Warwick, 1982
- **Fads & Fashions: Track 24**
1) Teddy Ruxpin
2) Polly Pocket
3) Katherine Hamnet
4) Kevin Keegan
5) McDonalds

- **Spot The Intro: Track 25**
1) Sign Your Name - Terence Trent D'Arby, 1988
2) Separate Lives - Phil Collins, 1985
3) Girls Just Want To Have Fun - Cyndi Lauper, 1984
4) Going Underground - The Jam, 1980
5) Cuddly Toy - Roachford, 1989
- **Events: Track 26**
1) Terry Waite
2) Nigel Lawson
3) General Belgrano
4) John Hinkley III
5) John McEnroe
- **Spot The Intro: Track 27**
1) Rio - Duran Duran, 1982
2) De Do Do Do, De Da Da Da - The Police, 1980
3) Funky Town - Lipps Inc, 1989
4) I Want Your Sex - George Michael, 1987
5) Everytime You Go Away - Paul Young, 1985

Game 4 Answers (tracks 28-36)

- **Spot The Intro: Track 28**
1) My Perfect Cousin - Undertones, 1980
2) Addicted To Love - Robert Palmer, 1986
3) There Must Be An Angel - Eurythmics, 1985
4) Road To Hell - Chris Rea, 1989
5) The Love Cats - The Cure, 1983
- **Music: Track 29**
1) 99
2) Kim Wilde
3) One Day In Your Life
4) Musical Youth
5) Ghostbusters
- **Spot The Intro: Track 30**
1) One More Night - Phil Collins, 1985
2) The Best - Tina Turner, 1989
3) Living In America - James Brown, 1986
4) One Love - Bob Marley & The Wailers, 1984
5) Club Tropicana - Wham!, 1983
- **TV & Film: Track 31**
1) The A Team
2) Steven Spielberg
3) The Majestics
4) Axel Foley
5) Miami Vice
- **Spot The Intro: Track 32**
1) Do You Really Want To Hurt Me - Culture Club, 1982
2) Together We Are Beautiful - Fern Kinney, 1980
3) Absolute Beginners - David Bowie, 1986
4) Good Thing Going (We've Got A) - Sugar Minott, 1981
5) Need You Tonight - INXS, 1988

- **Fads & Fashions: Track 33**
1) He-Man
2) The Metro
3) Clive Sinclair
4) The wheel clamp
5) Virgin Atlantic
- **Spot The Intro: Track 34**
1) White Lines - Grandmaster Flash & Melle Mel, 1983
2) Blue Monday - New Order, 1983
3) Dressed For Success - Roxette, 1989
4) State Of Independence - Donna Summer, 1982
5) Tainted Love - Soft Cell, 1981
- **Events: Track 35**
1) The Pope (John Paul II)
2) Chris Bonington
3) John Lennon
4) Italy
5) The dog licence
- **Spot The Intro: Track 36**
1) Xanadu - Olivia Newton-John and ELO, 1980
2) Material Girl - Madonna, 1985
3) Being With You - Smokey Robinson, 1981
4) Woman In Love - Barbra Streisand, 1980
5) Look Of Love - ABC, 1982

Game 5 Answers (tracks 37-45)

- **Spot The Intro: Track 37**
1) Winner Takes It All - ABBA, 1980
2) Jealous Guy - Roxy Music, 1981
3) A Groovy Kind Of Love - Phil Collins, 1988
4) Suburbia - Pet Shop Boys, 1986
5) Enola Gay - Orchestral Manoeuvres In The Dark, 1980
- **Music: Track 38**
1) Careless Whisper
2) Paul McCartney
3) Phil Collins, in the Live Aid concert
4) Down the Chip Shop
5) 1982
- **Spot The Intro: Track 39**
1) Use It Up & Wear It Out - Odyssey, 1980
2) Down Under - Men At Work, 1983
3) Japanese Boy - Aneka, 1981
4) Right Back Where We Started From - Sinitta, 1989
5) I Feel For You - Chaka Khan, 1984
- **TV & Film: Track 40**
1) Glenn Close
2) Bodie and Doyle
3) Michelangelo, Leonardo, Donatello and Raphael
4) Rosanne Barr
5) Sir John Gielgud

- **Spot The Intro: Track 41**
1) Start! - The Jam, 1980
2) You Spin Me Round (Like A Record) - Dead or Alive, 1985
3) The Look - Roxette, 1989
4) Take On Me - A-ha, 1985
5) Invisible Sun - The Police, 1981
- **Fads & Fashions: Track 42**
1) Cabbage Patch Dolls
2) The Game Boy
3) Izod
4) The compact disc
5) Commodore 64
- **Spot The Intro: Track 43**
1) Ant Music - Adam & The Ants, 1980
2) Move Closer - Phyllis Nelson, 1985
3) A Good Heart - Feargal Sharkey, 1985
4) Self Control - Laura Branigan, 1984
5) Opportunities (Let's Make Lots Of Money) - Pet Shop Boys, '86
- **Events: Track 44**
1) Corporal punishment
2) The Queen's, at Buckingham Palace
3) Derek Hatton
4) Stonehenge
5) 1981
- **Spot The Intro: Track 45**
1) Bad Boys - Wham!, 1983
2) Borderline - Madonna, 1986
3) Safety Dance - Men Without Hats, 1983
4) Twisting By The Pool - Dire Straits, 1983
5) Don't You (Forget About Me) - Simple Minds, 1985

Game 6 Answers (tracks 46-54)

- **Spot The Intro: Track 46**
1) Ghost Town - The Specials, 1981
2) Beat It - Michael Jackson, 1983
3) The Model - Kraftwerk, 1981
4) Holding Out For A Hero - Bonnie Tyler, 1985
5) Kids In America - Kim Wilde, 1981
- **Music: Track 47**
1) Julio Iglesias
2) Nick Heyward
3) Andrew Ridgeley
4) Shaddap You Face (Joe Dolce Music Theatre)
5) 19
- **Spot The Intro: Track 48**
1) Super Trouper - ABBA, 1980
2) Another Day In Paradise - Phil Collins, 1989
3) Ain't Nobody - Chaka Khan, 1984
4) Chi Mai - Ennio Morricone, 1981
5) Relax - Frankie Goes To Hollywood, 1983

- **TV & Film: Track 49**
1) It'll Be Alright On The Night
2) Tom Cruise and Dustin Hoffman
3) My Wife Next Door
4) Vangelis
5) She was a keep-fit instructor

- **Spot The Intro: Track 50**
1) What Have I Done To Deserve This? - Pet Shop Boys, 1987
2) (Sexual) Healing - Marvin Gaye, 1982
3) Masterblaster - Stevie Wonder, 1980
4) Prince Charming - Adam & The Ants, 1981
5) Money For Nothing - Dire Straits, 1985

- **Fads & Fashions: Track 51**
1) The Smurfs
2) Transformers
3) Pac-Man
4) Trivial Pursuit
5) Moon-walking

- **Spot The Intro: Track 52**
1) Happy Talk - Captain Sensible, 1982
2) True Blue - Madonna, 1986
3) Spirits In A Material Word - The Police, 1981
4) Respectable - Mel & Kim, 1987
5) You Can't Hurry Love - Phil Collins, 1982

- **Events: Track 53**
1) King's Cross
2) Strategic Defense Initiative
3) Los Angeles Olympics
4) Peter Shilton
5) Guillotine

- **Spot The Intro: Track 54**
1) 99 Red Balloons - Nena, 1984
2) Atmosphere - Russ Abbot, 1984
3) Star Trekkin' - The Firm, 1987
4) Two Tribes - Frankie Goes To Hollywood, 1984
5) Temptation - Heaven 17, 1983

Game 7 Answers (tracks 55-63)

- **Spot The Intro: Track 55**
1) I've Never Been To Me - Charlene, 1982
2) Every Little Thing She Does Is Magic - The Police, 1981
3) Walk The Dinosaur - Was Not Was, 1987
4) Never Too Late - Kylie Minogue, 1989
5) Sealed With A Kiss - Jason Donovan, 1989

- **Music: Track 56**
1) Marvin Gaye
2) Siouxsie and the Banshees
3) Chris Rea
4) U2
5) Men At Work

- **Spot The Intro: Track 57**
1) Goody Two Shoes - Adam Ant, 1982
2) The Land Of Make Believe - Bucks Fizz, 1982
3) French Kissin' In The USA - Deborah Harry, 1986
4) You Got It (The Right Stuff) - New Kids On The Block, 1989
5) Jump - Van Halen, 1984

- **TV & Film: Track 58**
1) Shirley MacLaine
2) Charlene
3) Ben Kingsley
4) David Jason
5) On Golden Pond

- **Spot The Intro: Track 59**
1) Freedom - Wham!, 1984
2) La Isla Bonita - Madonna, 1987
3) I Want To Know What Love Is - Foreigner, 1985
4) For Your Eyes Only - Sheena Easton, 1981
5) Maneater - Daryl Hall and John Oates, 1982

- **Fads & Fashions: Track 60**
1) Pump dispensers
2) Power dressing
3) NutraSweet
4) Jane Fonda
5) Digital Audio Tape

- **Spot The Intro: Track 61**
1) Billie Jean - Michael Jackson, 1983
2) Town Called Malice - The Jam, 1982
3) When Love Comes To Town - U2, 1989
4) Smooth Operater - Sade, 1984
5) Golden Brown - The Stranglers, 1982

- **Events: Track 62**
1) York Minster
2) 1986
3) 'Irises' by Van Gogh
4) She gave birth to sextuplets
5) F.W. de Klerk

- **Spot The Intro: Track 63**
1) Power Of Love - Jennifer Rush, 1985
2) Happy Hour - Housemartins, 1986
3) Everything I Own - Boy George, 1987
4) Born To Run - Bruce Springsteen, 1987
15) I Just Called To Say I Love You - Stevie Wonder, 1984

Game 8 Answers (tracks 64-72)

- **Spot The Intro: Track 64**
1) Sun Always Shines On TV - A-ha, 1985
2) Hello - Lionel Richie, 1984
3) Wrapped Around Your Finger - The Police, 1983
4) Wonderful Life - Black, 1986
5) Sign Of The Times - Belle Stars, 1983

Game 8 Answers (continued)

- **Music: Track 65**
1) Cyndi Lauper
2) Philip Bailey
3) The Bangles
4) Flying Pickets
5) Karma Chameleon

- **Spot The Intro: Track 66**
1) Driving In My Car - Madness, 1982
2) Just Can't Stop Loving You - Michael Jackson, 1987
3) Can't Stay Away From You - Gloria Estefan, 1989
4) Rip It Up - Orange Juice, 1983
5) Physical - Olivia Newton-John, 1981

- **TV & Film: Track 67**
1) Fred Housego
2) Kenneth Williams
3) "I could be so good for you"
4) Cry Freedom
5) Terry Wogan

- **Spot The Intro: Track 68**
1) Feels Like I'm In Love - Kelly Marie, 1980
2) Je Ne Sais Pas Pourquoi - Kylie Minogue, 1988
3) Dancing With Tears In My Eyes - Ultravox, 1984
4) Ghostbusters - Ray Parker Junior, 1984
5) West End Girls - Pet Shop Boys, 1985

- **Fads & Fashions: Track 69**
1) My Little Pony
2) Penny Loafers
3) Button fly
4) Swatch
5) Mario Brothers

- **Spot The Intro: Track 70**
1) Don't Stand So Close To Me - Police, 1980
2) We Don't Need Another Hero - Tina Turner, 1985
3) I'm Gonna Be (500 Miles) - Proclaimers, 1988
4) I Eat Cannibals - Toto Coelo, 1982
5) Shaddap You Face - Joe Dolce Music Theatre, 1981

- **Events: Track 71**
1) John Major
2) Hitler's
3) The Sahara
4) Brighton
5) The Channel Tunnel

- **Spot The Intro: Track 72**
1) Turning Japanese - Vapors, 1980
2) View To A Kill - Duran Duran, 1985
3) I Owe You Nothing - Bros, 1988
4) 1999 - Prince, 1983
5) Coward Of The County - Kenny Rogers, 1980

Game 9 Answers (tracks 73-81)

- **Spot The Intro: Track 73**
1) The Way You Make Me Feel - Michael Jackson, 1987
2) Born In The USA - Bruce Springsteen, 1985
3) Where Do Broken Hearts Go? - Whitney Houston, 1988
4) Flashdance - Irene Cara, 1983
5) Pride (In The Name Of Love) - U2, 1984

- **Music: Track 74**
1) The Beat
2) Relax
3) Russ Abbott
4) Belinda Carlisle
5) Mel & Kim

- **Spot The Intro: Track 75**
1) Geno - Dexy's Midnight Runners, 1980
2) Too Shy - Kajagoogoo, 1983
3) Express Yourself - Madonna, 1989
4) An Innocent Man - Billy Joel, 1984
5) Is There Something I Should Know - Duran Duran, 1983

- **TV & Film: Track 76**
1) View To A Kill
2) Zaphod Beeblebrox
3) The Elephant Man
4) KITT
5) Debra Winger

- **Spot The Intro: Track 77**
1) Edge Of Heaven - Wham!, 1986
2) I Know Him So Well - Elaine Paige/Barbara Dickson, 1985
3) Take My Breath Away - Berlin, 1986
4) Man In The Mirror - Michael Jackson, 1988
5) Always On My Mind - Pet Shop Boys, 1987

- **Fads & Fashions: Track 78**
1) Friendship bracelets
2) Care Bears
3) 1984
4) The Laser Disc
5) Benetton

- **Spot The Intro: Track 79**
1) The Final Countdown - Europe, 1986
2) Knew You Were Waiting (For Me) - Franklin/Michael, 1987
3) Too Much Too Young - The Specials, 1980
4) You'll Never Stop Me Loving You - Sonia, 1989
5) Making Your Mind Up - Bucks Fizz, 1981

- **Events: Track 80**
1) British Gas
2) Broccoli
3) The Royal Marines
4) The Derby
5) Challenger

- **Spot The Intro: Track 81**
1) Rock Me Amadeus - Falco, 1986
2) Wanna Be Starting Something - Michael Jackson, 1983
3) Who Wants to Live Forever - Queen, 1986
4) Crying - Don McLean, 1980
5) Don't You Want Me - Human League, 1981

Game 10 Answers (tracks 82-90)

- **Spot The Intro: Track 82**
1) Fantasy Island - Tight Fit, 1982
2) Working My Way Back To You - Detroit Spinners, 1980
3) I'm Your Man - Wham!, 1985
4) 9 To 5 - Sheena Easton, 1980
5) Our House - Madness, 1982

- **Music: Track 83**
1) Eurythimics
2) Roland Rat
3) Dancing In The Street
4) Dexy's Midnight Runners
5) A-ha

- **Spot The Intro: Track 84**
1) Caravan Of Love - Housemartins, 1986
2) When The Going Gets Tough - Billy Ocean, 1986
3) The Reflex - Duran Duran, 1984
4) 1 2 3 - Gloria Estefan, 1988
5) Going Back To My Roots - Odyssey, 1981

- **TV & Film: Track 85**
1) Yellowcoats
2) Zelig
3) The Young Ones
4) When Harry Met Sally
5) A Gremlin

- **Spot The Intro: Track 86**
1) Whole Of The Moon - Waterboys, 1985
2) Never Gonna Give You Up - Rick Astley, 1987
3) China In Your Hand - T'Pau, 1987
4) Robert De Niro's Waiting - Bananarama, 1984
5) Start Me Up - Rolling Stones, 1981

- **Fads & Fashions: Track 87**
1) Worldwide Wrestling Federation
2) The pony tail
3) Calvin Klein
4) Wendy's
5) Nintendo

- **Spot The Intro: Track 88**
1) Like A Prayer - Madonna, 1989
2) Call Me - Blondie, 1980
3) Glory Of Love - Peter Cetera, 1986
4) Wild Boys - Duran Duran, 1984
5) China Girl - David Bowie, 1983

- **Events: Track 89**
1) 1983
2) Ian Botham
3) Rainbow Warrior
4) Tiananmen Square
5) Peter Wright

- **Spot The Intro: Track 90**
1) Ride On Time - Black Box, 1989
2) Love Plus One - Haircut 100, 1982
3) Get Out Of My Dreams - Billy Ocean, 1988
4) Careless Whisper - George Michael, 1984
5) Driving Home For Christmas - Chris Rea, 1988

Other Spot the Intro Games:

Other **BOOK TITLES**: 1960s and 1970s:

BOXED GAMES:

Please visit www.cheatwell.com for more details

Spot The Intro © 2008 Cheatwell Games

The following page contains the legal/copyright information for each of the SPOT THE INTRO round tracks in the order they occur on the audio CD. The information for each track in a round is separated by a semi-colon.

(Rowland/Paterson/Adams) © EMI Music Publishing Ltd/Kevin Adams Musis Ltd; (Stock/Aitken/Waterman) © Mike Stock Publishing/Universal Music Publishing Ltd/All Boys Music Ltd; (Allen/Bacharach/Cross/Bayer) © Warner Chappell; (Christopher) © Controversy Music; (Gibb/Gibb/Gibb) © BMG Music; (Joel) © EMI Songs Ltd; (Bates/Le Bon/Taylor/Taylor/Taylor) © Gloucester Place Music Ltd; (Stein/Harry) © Chrysalis Music Ltd; (Bailey/East/Collins) © Hit & Run Music(Publishing) Ltd/Notting Hill Music (UK) Ltd/BMG Music Publ Ltd; (Sumner) © GM Sumner; (Roberts/Sager) © Carlin Music Corp/Sony ATV Music Publishing (UK)/EMI Songs Ltd; (De Burgh) © Rondor Music (London) Ltd; (Steinman) © Carlin Music Corp; (De Shannon/Weiss) © Warner Chappell Artemis Music; (Nowles/Shipley) © Spirit Music Publishing Ltd/EMI Virgin Music Ltd; (Lennox/Stewart) © BMG Music Publ Ltd; (Gamble/Huff/Gilbert) © Warner Chappell North America; (White/Vaughn) © Campbell Connelly & Co Ltd/EMI Music Publishing Ltd; (Coverdale/Marsden) © EMI Music Publishing Ltd/Warner Chappell Music Ltd; (Jabara/Shaffer) © Warner Chappell North America/EMI Songs Ltd; (Rhodes/Le Beon/Taylor/Taylor/Taylor) © Gloucester Place Music Ltd; (Allen/Cann/Currie/Ure) © Universal Music Publishing Ltd; (Hodgens/Fahey/Valentino) © Universal-Amxious Music Ltd/Hornall Brother Music Ltd/Reverb Music Ltd; (Cook/Hyman/Farren/Kane/Marson/Sayag/Stewart/Trendle) © Magnet Music Ltd; (Weller) © Notting Hill Music; (Allison/Curtis) © Peermusic (UK) Ltd; (White/Fry/Singleton/Lickley) © EMI 10 Music Ltd; (Idol) © Chrysalis Music Ltd; (Clarke) © Sony Music Publishing (UK) Ltd; (Blackman/Jenkins) © Universal Music Publising Ltd; (Holly/O Toole/Nash/Gill) © Perfect Songs Ltd; (Steinberg/Kelly) © Sony-ATV Music Publihsing (UK); (Temperton) © Chrysalis Music Ltd; (O'Dowd/Moss/Hay/Craig/Pickett) © EMI Virgin Music Ltd/BMG Music Publ Ltd; (Gabriel) © Real World Music Ltd ; (Gordy/Carlo) © Burlington Music Co Ltd; (Ryan/Ryan/Brennan) © EMI Music Publishing Ltd; (Marley/) © Blue Mountain Music Ltd; (Joel) © EMI Music Publishing Ltd; (Lennon) © Lenono Music; (Stansfield/Devaney/Morris) © BMG Music Publ Ltd; (Michael) © Warner Chappell Music Ltd; (Holt/Barrett/Evans) © Sparta Florida Music Group Ltd; (Bigazzi/Tozzi/Veitch) © SIAE/Bucks Music Group Ltd/Sugar Songs UK Ltd; (Trad/Kerr/Burchill/MC Neil) © EMI Virgin Music Ltd; (Stevens/Hudson) © SonyATV Music Publishing Ltd; (Bowie) © EMI Music Publishing Ltd/RZO Music Ltd; (Adams/Vallance) © Rondor Music(London) Ltd/Universal Music Publishing Ltd; (Sternberg) © Peermusic (UK) Ltd; (Nevin) © Universal MCA Music Ltd; (Kershaw) © Rondor Music (London) Ltd; (Gaye/Whitfield/Strong) © Jobete Music/EMI Music; (Deane/Jaymes) © Chrysalis Music Ltd/EMI Songs Ltd; (Peters) © IQ Music Ltd; (Collins) © Hit & Run Music (Publishing) Ltd; (Gamble/Huff) © Warner Chappell North America; (Bowie/Mercury/Taylor/May/Deacon) © EMI Music Publishing Ltd/Queen Music Ltd/RZO Music Ltd; (Nelson) © Universal MCA Music Ltd; (Kluger/Bangalter/Byl) © Chelsea Music Publishing Co Ltd; (Bailey/ Currie/Leeway) © Point Music; (Peterik/Sullivan) © Warner Chappell North America/Famous Music Publishing Ltd; (Kemp) © Reformation Publishing Co Ltd; (Sumner) © GM Sumner; (Stewart/Lennox) © BMG Music Publ Ltd; (Gibb/Gibb/Gibb) © Warner Chappell Music Ltd/BMG Music Publ Ltd ; (D'arby) © EMI Virgin Music; (Bishop) © Hit & Run Music (Publishing) Ltd/EMI Music Publishing Ltd/Universal MCA Music Ltd; (Hazard) © Sony/ATV Music Publishing (UK); (Weller) © BMG Music Publ Ltd; (Roachford) © Universal Music; (Bates/Le Bon/Taylor/Taylor/Taylor) © Gloucester Place Music Ltd; (Sumner) © GM Sumner; (Greenbergs) © Warner Chappell North America; (Hall) © Warner Chappell Music Ltd/Warner Chappell North America; (Hall) © Warner Chappell; (O Neil/Bradley) © Universal MCA Music Ltd; (Palmer) © Warner Chappell North America; (Stewart/Lennox) © BMG Music Publ Ltd; (Rea) © Magnet Music Ltd; (Smith) © Fiction Songs Ltd; (Collins) © Hit & Run Music (Publishing) Ltd; (Knight/Chapman) © Finchley Music Publishing Ltd/I Q Music Ltd; (Midnight/Hartman) © EMI Songs Ltd; (Marley/) © Blue Mountain Music Ltd; (Michael/Ridgeley) © Morrison Leahy Music; (O'Dowd/Moss/Hay/Craig/) © EMI Virgin Music Ltd; (Leray) © Sony Music Publishing (UK) Ltd; (Bowie)c RZO Music Ltd; (King) © Apace Music Ltd; (Farris/Hutchence) © Warner Chappell; (Robinson/Glover) © IQ Music Ltd; (Morris/Hook/Dickin/Gilbert) © Warner Chappell Music Ltd; (Gessle) © EMI Music Publishing Ltd; (Vangelis/Anderson) © EMI Music Publishing Ltd/Warner Chappell North America; (Cobb) © Burlington Music Co Ltd; (Brown/Rans) © EMI Music Publishing Ltd; (Robinson) © Jobete Music/EMI Music; (Gibb/Gibb/Gibb) © Warner Chappell Music Ltd/BMG Music Publishing Ltd; (Palmer/ White/ Fry/Singleton) © EMI 10 Music Ltd; (Andersson/ Ulvaeus) © Bocu Music Ltd; (Lennon) © Lenono Music; (Sager/Wine) © Screen Gems-EMI Music Ltd; (Lowe/Tennant) © Sony ATV Music Publishing (UK); (McCluskey) © EMI Virgin Music; (Brown/Linzer) © Peermusic (UK) Ltd; (Hay/Strykert) © EMI Songs Ltd; (Heatlie) © EMI Music Publishing Ltd; (Tubbs/Edwards) © Chelsea Music Publishing Co Ltd/Sony/ATV Music Publishing (UK); (Nelson) © Universal MCA Music Ltd; (McCutcheon) © Garber Music; (Burns/ Percy/ Coy/ Lever) © Warner Chappell Music Ltd/Westbury Music Ltd; (Gessle) © EMI Music Publishing Ltd; (Waaktaar/Furuholmen/Harket) © EMI Music Publishing (UK); (Sumner) © GM Sumner; (Ant/Pirroni) © BMG Music Publishing Ltd; (Nelson) © IQ Music Ltd; (Mc Kee) © BUG Music Ltd; (Bigazzi/Riefoli/Piccolo) © SIAE/Sugar Songs UK Ltd; (Tennant/Lowe) © Sony ATV Music Publishing (UK); (Michael) © Morrison Leahy Music Ltd; (Lucas) © BMG Music Publishing Ltd; (Doroschuk) © Universal Music Publishing Ltd; (Knopfler) © Rondor Music (London) Ltd; (Forsey/Schiff) © Universal MCA Music; (Dammers) © Plangent Visions Music Ltd; (Jackson) © Warner Chappell North America; (Hutter/Bartos/Scult) © EMI Music Publishing Ltd; (Steinman/Pitchford) © Famous Music Publishing Ltd; (Wilde/Wilde) © Rak Publishing Ltd; (Andersson/Ulvaeus) © Bocu Music Ltd; (Collins) © Hit & Run Music (Publishing) Ltd; (Wolinski) © EMI Music Publishing Ltd; (Morricone) © SIAE/General Music U.K. Ltd; (Holly/O Toole/Gill) © Perfect Songs Ltd; (Willis/Tennant/Lowe) © Sony ATV Music Publishing (UK) / Universal MCA Music Ltd; (Gaye/Brown/Ritz) © EMI Songs Ltd; (Wonder) © Jobete Music/EMI Music; (Ant/Pirroni) © BMG Music Publishing Ltd; (Knopfler/Sumner) © Magnetic Publishing/ Rondor Music ; (Rodgers/Hammerstein) © EMI Music Publishing Ltd; (Ciccone/Bray) © Warner Chappell North America/Universal Musical Music Ltd; (Sumner) © GM Sumner; (Stock/Aitken/Waterman) © Sony ATV Music Publishing (UK)/Universal Music Publishing Ltd/All Boys Music Ltd; (Holland/Dozier/Holland) © Jobete Music (UK) Ltd; (Fahrenkrog-Petersen/Karges/McAlea) © EMI Songs Ltd; (Tucker/Findon/Rodway) © EMI Music Publishing (WP) Ltd; (Lister/O Connor/Kehoe) © Rory Martin Kehoe/Bark Music/Bushranger Music; (Johnson/O Toole/Gill) © Perfect Songs Ltd; (Gregory/Marsh/Ware) © EMI Virgin Music Ltd/Warner Chappell Music Ltd; (Miller/Hirsch) © Jobete Music/EMI Music; (Sumner) © GM Sumner; (Was/Was/Jacobs) © Universal MCA Music Ltd; (Stock/Aitken/Waterman) © Sony ATV Music Publishing (UK)/Universal Music Publishing Ltd/All Boys Music Ltd; (Geld/Udell) © Warner Chappell North America; (Ant/Pirroni) © BMG Music Publishing Ltd; (Hill/Sinfield) © EMI Virgin Music/BMG Music Publishing ; (Lorre) © EMI Music Publishing Ltd; (Starr) © EMI Songs Ltd; (Van Halen/Van Halen/Roth) © Chrysalis Music Ltd/Warner Chappell North America); (Michael) © Morrison Leahy Music Ltd; (Leonard/Ciccone/Gaitsch) © EMI Music Publishing Ltd/Warner Chappell North America/Sony-ATV Music Publishing (UK); (Jones) © Warner Chappell; (Conti/Leeson) © EMI United Partnership Ltd; (Allen/Hall/Oates) © Intersong Music Ltd/I Q Music Ltd; (Jackson) © Warner Chappell North America; (Weller) © BMG Music Publ Ltd; (Clayton/Evans/Hewson/Mullen) © Blue Mountain Music Ltd; (Adu/St John) © Peermusic (UK) Ltd/Sony Music Publishing (UK) Ltd; (Burnell/Cornwell/Black/Greenfield) © EMI Songs Ltd/Compete Music Ltd; (Rouge/Mende/Klopprogge/Rush) © GEMA/EMI Songs Ltd; (Unknown) © Copyright Control; (Gates) © Sony-ATV Music Publishing Ltd; (Springsteen) © Bruce Springsteen Zomba Music; (Wonder) © Jobete Music; (Waaktaar) © Sony ATV Music Publishing (UK); (Richie) © Rondor Music; (Sumner) © GM Sumner; (Vearncombe) © Hornall Brothers Music Ltd; (Parsons/ Barker/ Matthias/Joyce/Owen/Shore/Hirst) © Chrysalis Music Ltd; (Barson) © EMI Music Publishing Ltd; (Jackson) © Warner Chappell North America; (Estefan) © Universal MCA Music Ltd; (Collins) © Universal Island Music Ltd; (Kipner/Shaddick) © EMI Music Publishing Ltd; (Dorset) © Sony-ATV Music Publishing (UK); (Stock/Aitken/Waterman) © Sony ATV Music Publishing (UK)/Universal Music Publishing Ltd//All Boys Music Ltd; (Ure/Cross/Currie/Cann) © Universal Music Publishing Ltd; (Parker) © I Q Music Ltd/EMI Music Publishing Ltd; (Tennant/Lowe) © Sony ATV Music Publishing (UK); (Sumner) © GM Sumner; (Lyle/Britten) © Warner Chappell North America/Hornall Brothers Music Ltd; (Reid/Reid) © Warner Chappell Music Ltd; (Blue/Greedus/Nicolson) © Sony Music Publishing (UK) Ltd/ I Q Music Ltd; (Dolce) © Leosong Copyright Service Ltd; (Fenton) © EMI Music Publishing Ltd; (Barry/Le Bon/Rhodes/Taylor/Taylor/Taylor) © Gloucester Place Music Ltd/EMI Songs Ltd; (Graham/Watkins) © EMI Virgin Music Ltd/Warner Chappell Music Ltd; (Nelson) © Universal MCA Music Ltd; (Bowlin/Wheeler) © BMG Music/ Universal MCA Music; (Jackson) © Warner Chappell North America; (Springsteen) © Bruce Springsteen Zomba Music; (Jackson/Wildhorn) © Chrysalis Music Ltd/Sony ATV Music Publishing (UK); (Moroder/Forsey/Cara) © GEMA/Chappell Music Ltd; (Mullen/Clayton/Evans/Hewson) © Vlue Mountain Music; (Rowland/Archer) © EMI Music Publishing Ltd; (Hamill/Beggs/Neale/Strode/Askew) © Gloucester Place Music Ltd; (Bray/Ciccone) © Warner Chappell North America/Universal Island Music Ltd; (Joel) © EMI Music Publishing Ltd; (Taylor/Bates/Le Bon/Taylor/Taylor) © Gloucester Place Music Ltd; (Michael) © Morrison Leahy Music Ltd; (Andersson/ Ulvaeus/ Rice) © Universal Music Publishing Ltd; (Moroder/Whitlock) © GEMA/Famous Music Publishing Limited/Warner Chappell North America; (Ballard/Garrett) © Cherry Lane Music Ltd/Universal MCA Music Ltd; (James/Christopher/Thompson) © Screen Gems/EMI Music/Chelsea Music Publishing; (Tempest) © EMI Music Publishing Ltd; (Morgan/Climie) © Chrysalis Music Ltd/Warner Chappell North America; (Dammers) © Plangent Visions Music Ltd; (Stock/Aitken/Waterman) © Sony ATV Music Publishing (UK)/Universal Music Publishing Ltd/All Boys Music Ltd; (Hill/Danter) © RAK Publishing Ltd/BMG Music Publ. Ltd ; (Bolland/Bolland/Hoelzel) © Johan Hoelzel/Copyright Control/The International Music Network; (Jackson) © Warner Chappell North America; (May) © Queen Music Ltd; (Orbison/Melson) © Acuff-Rose Music Ltd/Universal MCA Music Ltd; (Callis/Oakey/Wright) © Warner Chappell/ EMI Songs; (Duiser/Souer) © GEMA/The International Music Network; (Linzer/Randell) © EMI Music Publishing Ltd/Screen Gems-EMI Music Ltd; (Michael) © Morrison Leahy Music Ltd; (Palmer) © Chappell Music Ltd; (Smyth/Foreman) © EMI Music Publishing Ltd; (Isley/Jasper/Isley) © Warner Chappell North America; (Brathwaite/Eastmond/Ocean/Lange) © Zomba Music Pub.Ltd; (Taylor/ Bates/ Le Bon/ Taylor/ Taylor) © Gloucester Place Music ; (Garcia/Estefan) © Universal MCA Music Ltd; (Dozier) © EMI Songs; (Scott) © Sony ATV Music; (Stock/Aitken/Waterman) © Sony ATV Music Publishing (UK)/Universal Music Publishing Ltd/All Boys Music Ltd; (Decker/Rogers) © BMG Music Publ. Ltd; (Swain/Jolley/Dallin/Woodward/Fahey) © EMI Music Publishing Ltd/Warner Chappell Music Ltd/Reverb Music Ltd; (Jagger/Richards) © Westminster Music; (Ciccone/Leonard) © Warner Chappell North America/EMI Music Publishing Ltd/SonyATV Music Publishing (UK); (Moroder/Taylor/Taylor/Taylor) © Chrysalis Music Ltd/Famous Music Publishing Limited; (Cetera/Foster/Nini) (c) Copyright Control/BMG Music Publ. Ltd/EMI Music Publishing Ltd/Peermusic (UK) Ltd; (Rhodes/Le Beon/Taylor/Taylor/Taylor) © Gloucester Place Music Ltd; (Bowie/Osterberg) © EMI Music Publishing Ltd/RZO Music Ltd/EMI Virgin Music Ltd; (Limoni/Daniela/Semplici/Hartman) © SIAE/MCA Music Ltd/MCS (Palan) / EMI Songs Ltd; (Heyward) © Bryan Morrison Music Ltd; (Ocean/Lange) © Zomba Music Pub.Ltd; (Michael/ Ridgeley) © Morrison Leahy Music Ltd/Warner Chappell Music Ltd; (Rea) © Magnet Music Ltd